WELL *with* GOD

AN 8 DIMENSIONAL APPROACH TO ACHIEVING
THE TOTAL LIFE WELLNESS GOD HAS FOR YOU!

WELL
with GOD

JULIE VAN ORDEN, MHA
Certified Wellness Practitioner
Faculty, Wellness Council of America

WELL *with* GOD

An 8 Dimensional Approach to Achieving The Total Life Wellness God Has For You!

ISBN (Print Edition): 978-1-7345378-0-2

ISBN (Kindle Edition): 978-1-7345378-1-9

Library of Congress Control Number (LCCN): 2020901139

Printed in the United States of America

Published by Julie Van Orden | Irving, Texas

Edited by Judy Jones

Prepared for publication by Palm Tree Productions | www.palmtreeproductions.com

To contact the author:
WELLWITHGOD.COM

DEDICATION

This book is dedicated to all who have heard there is a "best self" living inside of you, yet you have searched to no avail. May WELL WITH GOD help you find the surrender your soul needs to let God lift you to your most excellent self. It truly is there and you really are fabulous!

PRAISE FOR WELL WITH GOD

To read this book is to walk hand-in-hand with the author on one side and God on the other. The Spiritual Wellness chapter struck me the hardest with a deep reflection on the "why" of wellness. This book is not just a reflection on how to live a wellness lifestyle with worship mixed in, it is a reflection on the root of why wellness exists, why it matters. "Without God infused in our being, there is no well-being." It is easy to see health, job fulfillment, finances and other challenges in our lives as many moving targets. The anecdotes and reflections of this book are a reminder that they are all linked and the Spiritual well-being is the glue that holds it all together. God is what holds it all together. Tackling these challenges is not just made possible through faith. Our personal relationship with God strengthens us to be victorious over our life and find the fulfillment we seek.

—ELISA, ENGINEER

I thoroughly enjoyed *Well With God*. It speaks to the heart of those who just need some direction, a place to start. I appreciated the author sharing her own life's struggles and successes as it made the book more personal and not strictly academic. What a great addition to my library.

—LEIGH, SMALL BUSINESS OWNER

This is a great book and a useful tool for everyone—men, women, the career person or the homemaker; those who know God and those still searching. The author gives encouraging and real suggestions on how to improve areas of my life with God's words as a reminder. I also appreciate the author's openness and honesty in telling her own life experiences and stories of others which makes her tools and tips relatable and practical. The Spiritual Wellness section was my favorite, reminding me to "Listen to God, be responsive to His cues, take action, and then let go of the outcome." The author is such a great role model for this and has an obvious deep love, honor and affection for God.

—KERRY, MOTHER, HOMEMAKER, BUSINESS PARTNER

Well With God is a true gem. It's a mini-manual of how to better all aspects of your life, achieve goals, and overcome setbacks. There are invaluable guidelines on conquering life by being grounded with God. The suggestions are fun, calming, and they work!

I love that the author color-coded the 8 dimensions, helping me envision my life as a kaleidoscope. A kaleidoscope, like life, changes constantly, but only works if God (The Light) is used as the source.

I highly recommend this book to all those seeking to heal all areas of their life by "closing the gap" of an unhealthy life to being *Well With God*. Every teen and young adult should read this book to start them off on the right path. I loved it!

—TYRA, FLIGHT ATTENDANT

In *Well With God*, the chapter on Financial Wellness clearly explains that God's plan for us is not to have stress in our lives—in particular, financial stress. Julie Van Orden perfectly explains how being a good steward of money, recognizing budgetary responsibility, and tithing with joy all open God's blessings which lead to stress-free financial freedom.

—DANNY, PROJECT MANAGER

I love the passion, wisdom, perspective, and willingness of the author to speak so openly. The word "hope" came to mind. I think hope will be transferred through *Well With God* in a very special and heightened way.

—KRISTINA, SR. GOVERNMENTAL AFFAIRS SPECIALIST

I love this book! The structure is marvelous with how the author ties every chapter together and has placed relevant Bible verses perfectly. I like the use of anecdotes to illustrate her meaning.

—KAREN, HOMEMAKER

I really related to the Social Wellness chapter. I used to work in the hospitality industry but when I re-married and moved from the city to the country I became a full-time stay at home mother and wife. I didn't realize how much those five years affected me until reading this book! I didn't make any true connections with the other mothers at my daughter's new school, I didn't have any "friends" to socialize with, I gained almost 40 pounds and really withdrew. Once we moved back to a large city a few years ago, I started to get involved again. We joined a club. I learned to play golf. I met my neighbors and now have a "tribe" of friends that I trust immensely and bring me so much joy! One of my new closest friends introduced us to their church and we love it! If we can't go, we actually watch the pastor on TV every Sunday morning. I am physically active and in great shape again. As soon as I read "tribe" I knew that for me, I need to stay connected in order for mind and body to stay healthy.

–JILL, MOTHER, WIFE, HOMEMAKER

Thank you, Mrs. Van Orden, for listening to the impressions that God has put in your heart! You have written a very insightful and thought-provoking book. I totally changed professions a few years ago, so Environmental Wellness and Occupational Wellness personally resonate with me.

–LYNN, RECEPTIONIST

Well With God is an inspiring, informative book with a good flow, and is easy to read and understand. The author is very adept at navigating the reader through the multiple wellness dimensions and showing how each dimension can and will be interconnected with other dimensions—and all centered on God. I believe that following the principles outlined in the book will lead readers to a balanced, spiritual, more rewarding life. I plan to keep my copy handy for those moments when life throws me a curve and I need a way to work through it. *Well With God* is a very uplifting life lesson that will benefit many people.

–JERRY, SUPERVISORY BORDER PATROL AGENT (RETIRED)

Well With God is a modern read rooted in scripture and brought to life by relatable examples. Ms. Van Orden takes us on a journey to help us find our best version of ourselves when we place God at the center. This life-transforming model easily translates to all aspects of life: financial, physical, work, environmental, spiritual, mental, and social. It is a necessary reminder that we are all part of something greater than ourselves.

It is written to readers of all generations. "Tend your spiritual soil" with *Well With God*.

–TERI, VICE PRESIDENT CONSULTING
AND BUSINESS DEVELOPMENT

I was truly blown away by how relatable and enlightening this material is on so many levels—most importantly, on a spiritual level. *Well With God* is a great book that will help take you to that next level in your spiritual walk in a useful and effective way. It's relatable, easy to follow, informative, and effective for believers of any tenure. This book has helped put a new perspective to concepts I had previously encountered yet not understood within myself and my spiritual walk such as self-efficacy and occupational wellness. The information and exercises provided help put your new-found knowledge to practice in a practical and easy way. I truly believe *Well With God* is a great tool and resource for non-believers as well as a must-have at any Bible study or small group. This powerful book will make you feel as if our Father is whispering to you through a friend saying "It is well."

–CINDY, HR SHARED SERVICES ASSOCIATE

ACKNOWLEDGEMENTS

GOD—thank you for interrupting my meditation that morning to tell me to write the book and thank you for bearing with me when I tried to argue with you that it wasn't a book that was in my heart, it was a training series. Only You knew it would be both!

DAN AND TESS—thank you for growing in the petri dish with me to live out the great family wellness experiment!

DAD, MOM (IN HEAVEN), TANA AND STEPHEN—thank you for treating the baby of the family special, probably at your own expense, so I could grow through our circumstances and blossom.

LEAH BROOKS—thank you for saying yes when I asked you to review my book. You are the epitome of a daughter of the King … and I'm not talking Elvis.

JUDY JONES, MY COUSIN—thank you for reigniting your literary gift to edit my book. I think it's very cool that you used your payment to buy yourself, and cousin, Teresa Nicholson, bicycles to enhance your well-being! That's the inspiration of WELL WITH GOD!

AUSTIN MILLER, LITERARY AGENT AT DUPREE MILLER & ASSOCIATES—although I chose a different publishing route, your words of encouragement were life when I was uncertain. Thank you!

JAN MILLER, FOUNDER AND CEO AT DUPREE MILLER & ASSOCIATES—you do not know me but I heard you speak at Love Your Life conference at Lakewood Church and you inspired me to send you a handbook I had written on a secular topic. Your rejection letter was so kind and you explained that you primarily publish spiritually-based books. I kept your letter, all-the-while telling myself I would never write a spiritual book to send you. Fortunately, God knew I would write one and Dupree Miller Associates was where I initially returned and received the encouragement

I needed to keep moving forward. Although I chose a different publishing route, I thank you!

WENDY K. WALTERS AND PALM TREE PRODUCTIONS—thank you for using your #neweyes to help me bring WELL WITH GOD to fruition, all while in the midst of a double lens transplant. Your story is a miracle and has taught me much. I got a front row seat to witness next level faith. You are not really Wendy K. Walters, you are Wendy OMG Walters – W.O.W.!

KITTIES—thank you for sitting with me while I write, meditate and sleep. I wish you enjoyed two-stepping with me a little more!

THANK YOU AND AMEN.

*Every good thing we ever dreamed
for ourselves is from God.*

*It is all part of the blueprint
He has created for us to attain
our purpose, our destiny.*

*This is from where those feelings
come. They are from God.*

This is why the WELL WITH
GOD *model puts God at
the core of well-being.*

–JULIE VAN ORDEN

CONTENTS

Chapter 1

ROOTED IN WELLNESS

*"He is before all things, and in Him
all things hold together."*
–COLOSSIANS 1:17, NIV

For years, I have been inspired by the quote, "Other things may change us but we begin and end with family," by author Anthony Brandt. It's so deep and concise. Then, I started reading the Bible and found, "*I am the Alpha and the Omega, the First and the Last, the Beginning and the End.*"[1] OMG! Literally, Oh My God! That is not just deep, it is rooted! It is profound! Rooted and profound wellness is what WELL WITH GOD seeks to inspire. Rooted because true and lasting well-being grows from the inside out. Profound because when we are rooted in wellness, we fervently seek it, all of it! *Ask and it will be given to you; seek and you will find; knock and the door will be opened to you.*[2] Now, close your eyes and take three slow, deep cleansing breaths—four counts in, hold it for four, and four counts out. Do this now. *Then the Lord God formed a man from the dust of the ground and breathed into his nostrils the breath of life, and the man became a living being.*[3] Now, let's get rooted in wellness together.

It became fashionable in the early 2000s to talk about achieving our "best self," followed in the 2010s by the concept of holistic wellness—a healthy mind, body and spirit. Holistic wellness is actually a retro concept that first surfaced in the 1970s, and that was when I drank the wellness Kool-Aid. I was around age 15, and I had this epiphany that the choices I made had a lot to do with the outcomes I would achieve in life. Prior to that, I was making some pretty bad choices at a pretty early age. Yet even in the middle of the bad choices, I had prevailing gut feelings, and at 15 I followed them in a hard, right turn onto a new path for myself.

A transformational path. A path where I would get a formal education in health, apply the concepts I learned to my own life and work to help inspire others to find their own transformation.

I had, *have*, always been led by my feelings. I called them gut feelings, then street smarts, then instincts. Finally I evolved into calling them intuition or a sixth sense. Later as my intuition led me to church, I was introduced to the concept that those impressions were the Holy Spirit, and finally, when I moved from religion to a relationship with God, I came to understand the Holy Spirit is the voice of God impressed upon me, and it is real, and it is not my voice but His, for me. *His, for you, too!*

You may be wondering, "What does God have to do with wellness?" The best way to answer that is to move away from a fragmented view of wellness into the big picture perspective. The big picture perspective is the key to rooting our wellness. Fragmented wellness is found in singular elements such as diets, exercise programs, biometric screening numbers, etc. In the corporate world it is found in terms like Return on Investment (ROI), Value on Investment (VOI) and efforts to drive-down employee health care costs, lower absenteeism, and drive-up productivity. Most singular elements focus on physical wellness and some dabble in mental well-being, but most people I have worked with are interested in transformational wellness; and transformation cannot be found in a diet, a biometric screening, or a stress management class all on their own.

The big picture perspective on wellness is a multi-dimensional model. That may seem like a whole lot more work since we already know the single element of dieting can be hard work. But the pursuit of wellness, once you understand it from the larger perspective, isn't about work—it is about living. Living from the inside out rather than the outside in. I'm not talking about a wellness "lifestyle." I am talking about rooted wellness that leads to fervently and joyfully seeking wellness and living well. So, the answer to the question, "What does God have to do with wellness?"

is answered in one of the dimensions of the multi-dimensional model—Spiritual Wellness. Spiritual Wellness is found in almost every credible model of wellness I have encountered. In Chapter Nine, I will share a perspective of Spiritual Wellness that goes beyond typical discussions and takes it straight to God. There we will revisit Jesus's words, *"Ask and it will be given to you; seek and you will find; knock and the door will be opened to you. For everyone who asks receives; the one who seeks finds; and to the one who knocks, the door will be opened."*[4] The remainder of this chapter will answer the question, "What is wellness?"

DEFINING WELLNESS

As a health and wellness professional for over 30 years, I can attest there are many models that describe what wellness is and what it includes. Some models are scientific and others are opinions or even fads. They are all generally positive and good, are intended to be helpful and steer us in the right direction for a healthy, happy, life and they do, *for the most part.* But, can you be satisfied with a *for the most part* level of wellness? Wellness is not just the absence of disease, a successful diet or an adequate antidepressant. Wellness suggests thriving and joy! Wellness does not exist in the *for the most part* realm. Wellness exists in the Divine realm, the God realm, in the place where we've done our part trying to achieve wellness and we've been as successful as our physical or mental ability will allow—and then God takes us to a new level, where we have joy and fulfillment that are hard to describe. All just because we asked Him for it.

I was once on an elevator and a woman stepped-in; and since I've never met a stranger, I greeted her with a friendly, "How are you today?" Her reply was a huge smile and a beaming, "I'm blessed and highly favored! Thank you for asking!" Now, I want some of that! That kind of joy does not exist in the natural! It *lives* in the supernatural, the Spiritual realm, the God realm. This woman was not particularly svelte, and she was not particularly overweight. I have no idea if she ate her granola that morning or meditated in prayer. What I do know is she filled the elevator with her joy, and it seeped into my spirit just being in her presence. If we are interested in that level of wellness, we cannot turn to a *for the most part* model; we need a supernatural model. WELL WITH GOD is that model!

IF WE ARE INTERESTED IN THAT LEVEL OF WELLNESS, WE CANNOT TURN TO A *FOR THE MOST PART* MODEL; WE NEED A SUPERNATURAL MODEL

Nearly all the wellness models I have seen and used throughout my career place the multi-dimensional elements of wellness in equal standing with each other, on a list or on a pie chart, in no particular order, including the Spiritual Wellness element. Until recently, it had not occurred to me to think differently about each element's standing. That is, until I experienced supernatural opportunities and supernatural closings-of-doors (more like slamming doors) in several of the other dimensions that were unexplainable. I simply could not make sense of what was happening, and I certainly could not take credit or blame for them, even though I tried to at times. This is when I shifted the way I visualized wellness models. This is when I moved Spiritual Wellness, God, to the center.

I remember being in a brainstorming session once with colleagues and I came up with an outreach idea that was a "Eureka!" moment. We were very excited and in full agreement to make that one of the projects we would request grant funds to implement. The whole time I was thinking, *Where did that come from?* It was more than just a good idea based on thinking creatively. It was a great concept and it simply came out of my mouth, from thin air, from God. It turned out to be a very successful campaign! This book is another good example. I was minding my own business, sitting in meditation asking God to take away the unbelievable anxiety I was experiencing over a particular person's behavior toward me at work, and He set it right down in the middle of my meditation: "Start writing the book. Today." I tried to negotiate in my head with God, *It isn't a book it is a training, God. ... and, by the way, I am on a completely different topic praying about work, not a project!* God laid it on my heart again and I resigned myself to trust Him, saying out loud in my otherwise unoccupied house, "Okay." Then, I proceeded to clean my house and about an hour later God nudged me with a gentle, "Go start." It was not an out-loud voice. Actually, it was a magazine that fell off an ottoman five feet away from me and I felt this impression, "Go start." So, I did. I sat down at my kitchen table, pulled out a rejection letter I had been holding onto from a literary agent. It was for a handbook I submitted three years earlier on a completely secular topic. This time, I emailed the agency and told them about a training I wanted to develop based on God-centered wellness. Less than 24 hours later I received an enthusiastic email, affirming me, expressing interest in a cautiously optimistic way, and requesting I submit my book proposal so they could learn more. I did not have a book proposal. I did not even know what a literary proposal should include, because the last time, I sent them the entire handbook with a cover letter. This time I asked, and they gave me some direction. I also researched online and now, here I am.

When I sat down to start the book, I thought, *What should I use for a working title?* The answer was an immediate impression on my spirit, "Why don't you use WELL WITH GOD, since you purchased a domain name a year ago, and started Twitter and Instagram accounts with the name?" I had done all that nearly a year earlier without any real direction toward writing a book. Back then, I was simply following God's direction—again. I had no plan, and the enemy tried to tell me I was conjuring up a pipe dream of developing a training series or maybe a book; but I just did what was laid on my heart and waited. Waited until God told me to start in the middle of a mediation months later, when I just wanted him to help me with a problem at work.

As I said earlier, Spiritual Wellness is part of most credible models of wellness. I have seen wellness models that have only three dimensions— mind, body and spirit, and others having as many as twelve dimensions. I have tended toward models that were developed by national organizations or educational institutions, because they are typically well-researched and basically trustworthy sources. One thing my favorite models have in common is they all include the same elements. They are just labeled differently, grouped, expanded or condensed, but they are all represented. The WELL WITH GOD model includes the same elements found in popular models, but I structure it differently, as I said, with God at the center. I label it "God" instead of "Spiritual," acknowledging that God is the source of the Spirit.

With God at the center, let me label and briefly define the dimensions of wellness here, tie them together, and follow-up with a chapter on each, including how you can live your personal WELL WITH GOD journey.

To date, I do not structure the WELL WITH GOD model any further than to put God at the center. The rest of the dimensions I place around the center in equal standing (and in no particular order), but all are interconnected. That could change at any time with another nudge from God, but for the purpose of the rest of this book, they are all of equal standing, yet interdependent on each other.

PHYSICAL WELLNESS

I like to start with **Physical Wellness** because most people think of this when they first think of wellness. For years, I have vacillated on whether to break this dimension into three independent dimensions, but for now I have decided to keep it consistent with the physical dimension as described by the national Substance Abuse and Mental Health Services Administration (SAMSHA) where Physical Wellness includes physical fitness, nutrition and sleep.

Nutrition and fitness, diet and exercise, is where a lot of people begin and end their wellness journey. The problem with this is there are many people who are physically fit, eat nutritiously and get 7-9 hours of sleep each night, but still live sad, depressed, empty, lonely, unfulfilled lives. Yet, when added to the bigger model of wellness, Physical Wellness is the proverbial *triple threat* and can be an excellent catalyst for success in the other areas. If you are naturally drawn to exercise, healthy eating and getting enough rest, this is a great benefit, not only because it is good for us, but because physical well-being is externally visible. Since much of our world is visual and we respond positively or negatively to things we see, you likely experience immediate gratification from others on a regular basis, or even from yourself as you look in the mirror each day, if what you see is healthy.

Inasmuch as Physical Wellness is a powerful dimension for the positive, it can have the opposite effect if you are not physically healthy or not taking care of your physical well-being. *Do you not know that your bodies are temples of the Holy Spirit, who is in you, whom you have received from God? You are not your own; you were bought at a price. Therefore honor God with your bodies.*[5]

FINANCIAL WELLNESS

Another powerhouse of the WELL WITH GOD model is **Financial Wellness**. Financial Wellness is not as much about the size of your bank account as it is about the quality of your financial habits. Like Physical Wellness, it can be outwardly recognized by others and invite positive benefits in the way people respond to you. While physical well-being may prompt compliments and admiration, financial well-being often attracts respect from others. Whether this is right or wrong does not change the fact that it is a reality. I make this point to emphasize that there are certain dimensions of wellness that attract affirmation in some form by others, and affirmation helps strengthen other dimensions of wellness, particularly Mental Wellness. This starts to show the interconnectedness of the dimensions, and how when one area is lacking, others can begin to suffer as a result until we are unwell in more areas than we are well.

Financial well-being is demonstrated personally by having a budget and exercising discipline with the budget. It is evident in our priorities with our money, which includes our attitude. It is evident in our planning in-the-now around expected and unexpected expenses and our preparedness for the future. *Suppose one of you wants to build a tower.*

Won't you first sit down and estimate the cost to see if you have enough money to complete it?[6]

MENTAL WELLNESS

Mental Wellness includes both mental and emotional well-being, but they are not the same thing. Emotional well-being can also be tied to emotional intelligence, another great concept that became most popular in the 1990s and 2000s. Resiliency, coping mechanisms, positive self-talk, and responding versus reacting to situations are all key indicators of mental well-being. Our Mental Wellness is interwoven with emotional wellness and emotional intelligence, which are evident in the way we relate with others, the way we speak, our confidence, our respect, and our inclusion.

I talk about Mental Wellness apart from mental illness because of the complexity of the clinical aspects related to mental illness, including chemical imbalances, trauma, tragedy, genetics, and other things beyond our personal control. If ever there was a time to turn to God, mental health issues are surely it. I do have faith that with good mental health care and with God, mental illness can be brought to a functional level of Mental Wellness. *Do not be anxious about anything, but in every situation, by prayer and petition, with thanksgiving, present your request to God. And the peace of God, which transcends all understanding, will guard your hearts and your minds in Christ Jesus.*[7]

ENVIRONMENTAL WELLNESS

When I talk about ***Environmental Wellness***, I am not talking so much about being "green"—recycling, conservation, and the like. Those are excellent things and are part of the more longitudinal look at

Environmental Wellness that I will expand upon in Chapter Five. First and foremost, I am referring to the quality of the environment in which we live and work from a culture perspective—not an ethnic culture, but the "vibe."

Is our environment at home and work harmonious? Are they toxic? Are they a place we can thrive, hold healthy conversations, experience growth, be authentic and discover our authentic self? Achieving environmental well-being unsurprisingly occurs in predominantly drama-free settings; and it is important that we have a high level of functionality in our home life, our social life and our work and/or school life, if we are to maximize our environmental well-being. If we have a work life where we are thriving but our home life is in chaos, our work/life balance gets unsettled, and depending on how we handle situations, we can easily make them mirror each other as one aspect of our life bleeds into the other. *The rain came down, the streams rose, and the winds blew and beat against the house; yet it did not fall, because it had its foundation on the rock.*[8]

When our Environmental Wellness is harmonious in all aspects of our lives, it becomes reflected in the physical settings. It allows us to create space to support our thriving, happy demeanor, both at home and in the workplace. We create order, and through order our emotional well-being is nurtured.

OCCUPATIONAL WELLNESS

I love *Occupational Wellness* because it is tied to seeking and discovering our anointed destiny in life! We spend so much of our life in our employment, and God does not intend our work to be drudgery.

He has set up each of us with an undeniable gift and a divine set of skills that, when we discover them and put them to work, it will feel like home. It will be effortless to execute.

One of the keys to finding our destiny is letting God lead us to it. He does this through offering us opportunity. Many people pass on the opportunity to step into their destiny because they do not recognize it as their destiny. They have in mind what they *want* to do and miss what they are *meant* to do. Challenges and obstacles count as opportunities as well. God allows them in our path so we can sharpen our skills and peel away our layers to reveal our gifts. But we often get mired in bitterness over obstacles, rejecting the opportunities they present, because we have too narrow a view of what opportunity is. The growth that occurs through adversity is undeniable, and although God may not take it away, He will take us through it, if we let Him. *Many are the plans in a person's heart, but it is the Lord's purpose that prevails.*[9]

We will know we have arrived to our divine work destination because we will feel absolutely, positively fulfilled, enriched and satisfied with what we are doing. We will also know because it will serve others, even though it may not be a job in the service industry. It will serve because our work destiny is to serve. It just shows-up in unexpected occupations, not just occupations in 501(c)3 businesses. My destiny happens to lie in the field of health and wellness, but there was a time I thought I would become a broadcast journalist. I started out majoring in broadcasting in college and switched to health science after three semesters. Six years after graduating, I was following my career path, helping vulnerable families learn to create healthier home environments, when God showed-up again in a profound way. The Director of our Center was approached to fill the 7 PM time-slot on Tuesday night local cable television. They wanted our Center to do a 30-minute educational show on healthy, productive parenting. I became the weekly co-host, and later, the regular fill-in as host. It was not national syndicated television. That would have served my ego. This was service! Instead of sharing news, I was sharing knowledge and experience. It supernaturally satisfied my desire to be in the public eye, but He refined my desire to make it worthy of Him. Who knew? God knew! God did that, not me. *For we are God's handiwork, created in Christ Jesus to do good works, which God prepared in advance for us to do.*[10]

INTELLECTUAL WELLNESS

I used to have trouble comprehending the difference between **Intellectual Wellness** and Occupational Wellness. The word "creative" helped me get past that. Intellectual Wellness can be closely tied to occupational when a person continually expands their knowledge to grow and create new and better ways to be effective in their employment.

But mostly, intellectual well-being is associated with staying creatively and intellectually stimulated, regardless of whether it supports our occupation. I used to come home from my Family Resource Center job, which I loved, and I would then design and sew clothes for my daughter and myself. If my husband and I were going to a costume party, you can be sure we would be entered to compete for the best costume. If we were going on vacation, I was working for weeks ahead of time to make cute outfits for our daughter to wear. If I saw cool fabric, all I could think about was, *What can I make with this?* I never wanted to turn it into a profession; I did it to stimulate my creative and intellectual self. My dad was a civil engineer and his creative outlet, unbeknownst to me for many years, was reading books on history and physics. It was not tied to his work; it was tied to his interest and served much like a hobby. Intellectual Wellness is found in our continued exercise to expand our knowledge and skills and to follow our interests. It is prompted by our curiosity. When we are intellectually stimulated and we feed our creative and intellectual mind, our self-esteem naturally elevates. Elevated self-esteem increases our mental well-being, and it also can increase our confidence in developing social connections with similar interests, thus improving our Social Wellness. *And he has filled him with the Spirit of God, with wisdom, with understanding, with knowledge and with all kinds of skills.*[11]

SOCIAL WELLNESS

Social Wellness is tribal. I love the word tribe. It sounds primitive, but it never goes out of style. We all need our tribe, our place we belong, where we feel we are understood and we offer understanding effortlessly and genuinely to the other members of our group. This is Social Wellness. It is our support system in addition to God. It is closely tied to environmental well-being in that we need to create environments in which to live and work that include healthy social supports, but it rounds out a triad of spaces we occupy where our Social Wellness is fed—home, work and society.

Social Wellness can be underestimated, which I discovered when my husband and I moved to live near our only child. Shortly after relocating, our daughter and her husband moved to another city, my husband's work transferred him to, yet, another city, and I stayed behind to sell our house while continuing to work and look for a job near my husband. It was a choice similar to others we had made in the past as a military family, but this time was different. This is where I had a profound introduction to the importance of having an adequate level of Social Wellness. I have always been a social person and have easily developed close relationships with others. In essence, I had easily established my tribe whenever we moved

15

to new locations. This time was different. I had so much change that occurred all at once. Our daughter was out of our nest and building her own nest with her own husband; my husband was out of the military and we were no longer living in a military community; and I was establishing relationships as a more mature woman, not my daughter's mother or my husband's wife, for the first time. I was very sad and depressed.

I started to find reasons not to exercise and increased the frequency of my visits to a certain fast food restaurant. I also became critical of my work, which I previously loved, and I worked with really wonderful people. My epiphany came when I was preparing a presentation on the dimensions of wellness for an upcoming conference. I created an assessment for my audience to apply to their employee wellness program. The goal was for them to determine what dimensions of wellness in their programming were the strongest and which needed work. I completed the exercise for my own institution, and then God nudged me to complete it as an individual, not a program manager, but my own personal assessment of what dimensions in my life were strongest and which needed improvement. I discovered immediately I had no cohesive tribe in my new town! I had a few good friends that I could talk to, but I only talked to each about certain things. I was withholding my whole self from the relationships, probably because I knew I would be moving and would need to find a new tribe.

This revelation allowed me to open myself more to the people who made up the tribe I would be leaving and the tribe I was starting to form in our new location. Once I got my social well-being back in check, my equilibrium returned. It was easier to stay committed to my diet and exercise and even my meditation practices, not because my tribe joined me in these endeavors but because my balance was restored. *"My command is this: Love each other as I have loved you. Greater love has no one than this: to lay down one's life for one's friends."* [12]

SPIRITUAL WELLNESS

Spiritual Wellness is recognized in that feeling that we are part of something greater than ourselves. The inner knowing that we have purpose and following those instincts, which are ultimately God speaking to us through the Holy Spirit.

In order to have Spiritual Wellness, we have to work out spiritually, just like we have to pump some iron if we want to build our muscles. As with exercise, there are a number of outlets for working-out with God. We can go to church, listen or watch online, attend Bible study, hold discussions, attend retreats, pray, journal, listen to praise music, give service and at minimum, we need to read His Word, the Bible.

Reading the Bible was an overwhelmingly daunting task for me, which is why it took me so long to do it. My problem was my approach. I attempted many times to read the Bible starting at the beginning. I never got far and I always gave-up. Until I attended a Bible study and a respected pastor was asked a question about how to read the Bible. She recommended starting with the New Testament, with Matthew, and reading one chapter a day, followed by one Proverb in the Old Testament for wisdom and one Psalm in the Old Testament for inspiration. This was like magic for me and filled a huge void in my Spiritual Wellness. If you struggle as I did with reading the Bible, I wholly recommend you try this, to see if it opens a new door for you too.

If we want to get healthy, if we want to be WELL WITH GOD, we have to put God first and we have to listen to Him. Listening to God and being disciplined to follow His Word are essential, but we must also take the next step and surrender to God's will, putting it all in His hands in an exercise of faith. Instead, we often get in our head and want to do the driving, and we stop listening to God. Be assured, there is a time to drive. That time is when God tells us to drive. When He presents an opportunity and wants us to step through the door. When he lays an idea or impression on us and wants us to act on it, now, not later, and certainly not never. Listening to God means we are responsive to his cues, we take action, then *let go* of the outcome. That last part is the hard part. We cannot just let it go *intellectually*, we have to let it go from the heart in a demonstration of faith. When we let it go intellectually, we are saying it in our head, but in our heart, we really want what we really want. When we let it go from the heart, we truly give it to God, and we really want what He really wants, knowing we may have to encounter impatience, ego, disappointment— the enemy, on the way to our destiny.

> LISTENING TO GOD MEANS WE ARE RESPONSIVE TO HIS CUES, WE TAKE ACTION, THEN LET GO OF THE OUTCOME.

Every good thing we ever dreamed for ourselves is from God. It is all part of the blueprint He has created for us to attain our purpose, our destiny. This is from where those feelings come. They are from God. This is why the WELL WITH GOD model puts God at the core of well-being. Every goal, every idea, every hope is from God, for us—every desire for that perfect job, to get back into a fitness routine, to start eating healthy, to stop being so stressed and live a happy life, to have a peaceful home or work environment. This is built-in desire for good things, built into us by God, to draw us to Him and receive everything good He has prepared for us. We need only ask Him, and not just mean it when we ask, but *know* it when we ask. Know that He has prepared it for us. Not just think he might possibly have prepared something, but we are not quite sure, so we are going to ask but not really expect much. *But seek first His kingdom and His righteousness, and all these things will be given to you as well.*[13]

Putting God (Spiritual) wellness at the end of the WELL WITH GOD discussion is the proverbial "last but not least" dimension of wellness. I put it last because it will be the most recent part of this book you have read, and the first thing you start with on your journey to well-being. **Rooted in wellness starts with being rooted with God.** We have to tend our Spiritual soil. Without tending our Spiritual soil, our roots wither, and little can grow, much less thrive. Everything good and exceptional that we see and experience on the surface of life is grown healthy and whole through the seed and well-tended soil of the fertile ground of God. Deep roots. Without them, we live mediocre. With them we are in Him and we are Well with God.

This is how we know
that we live in him and he in us:
He has given us of his Spirit.
1 JOHN 4:13, NIV

YOUR WELL WITH GOD JOURNEY

By the end of reading WELL WITH GOD, you will understand the eight dimensions of wellness:

- PHYSICAL WELLNESS

- FINANCIAL WELLNESS

- MENTAL WELLNESS

- ENVIRONMENTAL WELLNESS

- OCCUPATIONAL WELLNESS

- INTELLECTUAL WELLNESS

- SOCIAL WELLNESS

- SPIRITUAL WELLNESS

You will have a vision for improving your own personal state of well-being. I will even go as far as predicting that you will begin to change in the process of reading WELL WITH GOD, and you will like your results!

Grab some paper and a pen because you will need them later as you take your wellness journey. Now, let us get WELL WITH GOD by starting with this prayer:

God, reveal to me the personal enlightenment you have waiting in this book. I am ready to receive it. Amen.

ENDNOTES

1. Revelation 22:13, NIV.

2. Matthew 7:7, NIV.

3. Genesis 2:7, NIV.

4. Matthew 7:7-8, NIV.

5. 1 Corinthians 6:19-20, NIV.

6. Luke 14:28, NIV.

7. Philippians 4:6-7, NIV.

8. Matthew 7:25, NIV.

9. Proverbs 19:21, NIV.

10. Ephesians 2:10, NIV.

11. Exodus 35:31, NIV.

12. John 15:12-13, NIV.

13. Matthew 6:33, NIV.

PHYSICAL WELLNESS

"Keep your vitality. A life without health
is like a river without water."

–MAXIME LAGACÉ

It is important to know that Physical Wellness is not just about exercise. It is not even just about dieting. This should be a relief to many who have already taken the diet and exercise journey, maybe more than once, and are frustrated and disillusioned that it did not work out or it did not last. According to several prevailing models, Physical Wellness includes three things: physical fitness, nutrition and sleep. But I do not want to start there. I want to start the discussion by talking about our DNA, literally and metaphorically, our God-given raw material. We are each unique and complex creations with physical DNA, personality DNA and destiny DNA. *Yet you, Lord, are our Father. We are the clay, you are the potter; we are all the work of your hand.*[1]

DNA is God's "Made by" tag. If we start with God uniquely making each of us, we have to approach our Physical Wellness potential by considering what our best version of fitness looks like according to the raw material with which He has blessed us. We have to look at ourselves and see our physical strengths—broad shoulders, natural curves, long and lanky, small and stocky, etc. Most of all, no comparisons. Then, we need to open our mind and know that what good vision we conjure-up is even better through God's eyes. He has knitted us together as an intricate and unique human being, of which there is no duplicate and no true comparison. Therefore, although we may have role-models we look to in our Physical Wellness journey, we have to approach the trip as a unique and exclusive path unto ourselves.

PHYSICAL FITNESS

Consider this: what if finding lasting success with fitness and weight loss is tied to your job (Occupational Wellness), or your current financial situation (Financial Wellness)? What if it is tied to your Mental Wellness or your Social Wellness? Let me share the story of Alexis. I met Alexis when she emailed me to thank me for a nutrition campaign I was promoting at our worksite. She had only a few more pounds to lose to meet her weight goal. For her 30th birthday, Alexis wanted to go skydiving! The only problem was when she started exploring companies that could take her on her skydiving adventure, she learned that they had a weight restriction. She could not weigh more than 250 lbs. Alexis weighed over 250 lbs. and expressed joyfully to me, "I've always been comfortable with my weight and my curves." Whether Alexis had failed diets in the past, I do not know. All I know is she was not motivated to lose weight this time until her weight became a barrier to an important personal goal. That goal was skydiving. By the time I launched our nutrition campaign at work, Alexis was well on her way to her weight loss goal and our new campaign gave her the extra tools she needed to get down to 250 lbs.—just in time to skydive for her thirtieth birthday!

I received photos from Alexis of the momentous skydiving occasion and it looked exhilarating. But the story does not end here. I had previously only corresponded with Alexis via email and phone calls. I had never met her in person. We worked in different buildings in the city, even though for the same organization. Approximately 11 months later, I was in Alexis's building on other business and I decided to look her up. When I met her in person, she was not the woman in the pictures she had previously sent. She was standing in front of me, literally radiating joy and well-under 250 lbs! I would estimate approximately 170 lbs. She declared, "I felt so good I just kept going!" Her physical well-being was all over her, her skin glowed, her eyes sparkled, her smile was contagious, her hair was a mass of curly brown perfection and her curves were still all there, under a colorful fitted work dress that declared, I am present and accounted for!

It is true Alexis used diet and exercise to achieve weight loss. The difference is, she used them as tools, not motivation. Alexis did not begin with diet and exercise (Physical Wellness) as a goal. She was not thinking, "I need to get in shape because, well, I know I'm overweight." She was not saying to herself, "the doctor said I need to lower my cholesterol or blood sugar, so I need to go on a diet." She was not even saying "I am going to my class reunion or dating this great person and want to look good." Alexis's journey began somewhere in her personality and destiny DNA. The goal was never to get into shape. Her motivation was to fulfill a personal inner desire, something planted deep inside her, not an intellectual goal, a heart's desire. The Bible includes some rather negative passages about the desires of the heart, but heart's desires are transformed when we are rooted in God. These desires of the heart are born of the spirit and planted in each of us by God. *Take delight in the Lord, and he will give you the desires of your heart.*[2] *May he give you the desire of your heart and make all your plans succeed.*[3]

Because we are each uniquely and wonderfully made by God, our heart's desires are individual to each of us. Some of us share common elements of the various desires of our heart and these are some of the reasons we have natural chemistry with others. Alexis's journey likely began with a heart's desire for adventure, spiritually planted as part of her personality DNA. It was also aided by a healthy dose of self-confidence (Mental Wellness) and reinforced afterward by a level of Social Wellness because it joined her with a relatively unique tribe of people who have skydived. Barring a change in the intensity of my own spirit of adventure, I doubt I will ever join that particular social group. Yet my spirit of adventure recognizes and relates to Alexis's. Adventure was a heart's desire and a gateway for Alexis to access a higher level of physical well-being. This can be a reminder to each of us that although we may share a common interest with others, for example getting into shape, the motivation for fulfilling those interests comes from a different seed planted in the desires of each one of our hearts by God. I never had a conversation with Alexis about her spiritual beliefs but I realize I do not have to know a person's spiritual beliefs to recognize God's work in their life or see God in them. I see Him everywhere I look. I bet you do too!

I DO NOT HAVE TO KNOW A PERSON'S SPIRITUAL BELIEFS TO RECOGNIZE GOD'S WORK IN THEIR LIFE OR SEE GOD IN THEM

When it comes to motivation to achieving Physical Wellness, if you are having difficulty attaining or maintaining your goals, I encourage you to look in places other than the obvious. Your motivation may be hidden in plain sight, found in an exciting work opportunity, in your competitive nature, in a cultural experience or even in the faces of your loved ones. It may not even be found in accessing something positive, it may be found in eliminating something negative. I have been motivated by fitness all my life, therefore it has not been as challenging for me to achieve as some of the other dimensions of wellness. Yet I have consistently had trouble with my motivation to exercise, eat nutritiously and get enough sleep whenever I am struggling with workplace "fit." My husband was in the armed forces for 21 years and we moved frequently. I always managed to find great employment opportunities to forward my career, but a few times, the "fit" wasn't quite right, so my Occupational Wellness was suffering. I inevitably coped by withdrawing from my after-work fitness routine in favor of going home each day and comforting myself with a familiar place on the sofa, a thoughtless television show and comfort food. When I finally made the connection, I stopped chastising myself for bad diet and exercise habits and I focused on improving my work situation. The result? A better work situation and a return to my regular patterns of fitness.

Still, motivation may not be something you can find; it may actually have to find you. Fred was a new grandfather who contacted me about ways to make his home smell fresher. He had recently quit smoking and wanted to eradicate the smell of tobacco smoke from his house. The motivation to quit smoking and remove the ever-present scent from his home, sadly, had nothing to do with the anti-smoking billboard campaign we implemented in the county tobacco control program I was managing. It had nothing to do with his epiphany that smoking could lead to lung cancer and a host of other really unhealthy physical wellness issues. The motivation came when his granddaughter visited his home and had a severe asthma attack brought on by the residual presence of smoke in his house. "She nearly died," he told me as his voice cracked into crying, "because of me." Fred quit smoking that day and never looked back. Fred's motivator? Not his own mortality but the mortality of his loved one. Family and other loved ones are part of our Social Wellness and are not just tied to the support we get from our close connections but also the support and love we give to them. Potentially, three lives were saved the day Fred quit smoking: his as the smoker, his granddaughter's from future asthma attacks and his wife as a second-hand smoke recipient. I am glad to report, they lived healthily ever after and his wife got a complete home make-over to remove the smell that persisted in their carpet, walls, drapes and furniture!

If your motivation to achieve Physical Wellness is not staring you in the face, I invite you to sit still and be with God and ask Him to help you tap into the desires He has placed in your heart for your true fulfillment. Listen with spiritual ears for the voice of God, the impressions He lays on your heart, the opportunities and cues He gives along the way. He may not tell you to train for a 10K or go on a diet, He may throw you a curve ball like He did with Alexis and Fred. Follow God's plan for you and as an extra gift, you will undoubtedly fulfill one or more of the other dimensions of well-being. Then, let the dominoes fall!

You may be wondering, "What exactly is the physical state God expects me to achieve?" His plan is the same for us all. *Therefore, I urge you, brothers and sisters, in view of God's mercy to offer your bodies as a living sacrifice, holy and pleasing to God—this is your true and proper worship.*[4] When I think about what this scripture could mean for my Physical Wellness, my mind's eye focuses squarely on the word holy. Holy, meaning sacred and revered. To treat our body as holy and revered is to treat it very well. These words suggest an action or behavior toward our body, not a destination. Therefore, maybe we would benefit by shifting our mindset from trying to reach a particular destination in our clothing size, cholesterol level, blood pressure, etc, and honor our body by what we put into it, what we expose it to, how we treat it and how we let others treat it. The improved biometric outcomes and the physical size of our body will then become a positive by-product of the behaviors, rather than the goal. Having the focus be on the shoulders of our daily behavior rather than a destination may seem like constant work that will never end, but when we are in alignment with God, life is easier not harder.

If physical well-being is your natural strong suit, or if you have already achieved it as a secondary gift of pursuing another dimension, like Alexis and Fred, use the advantage. Because physical well-being is externally visible, it invites affirmation, not just from others, but more importantly from ourselves every day when we look in the mirror. Physical well-being can lead to higher self-esteem, attracting better occupational opportunities, improved financial outlook, greater intellectual creativity, improved social circles and more selectiveness in our personal environment. Thus, the domino effect. From another perspective, it may also lead us to not expand our horizons but to find the fulfillment we seek right where we are. Either way, we win in our journey for well-being!

Just as our physical state can be an excellent catalyst for success in the other dimensions it can also affect the other elements in our life in the opposite direction—a reverse domino effect. I once looked at myself in the mirror and off-handedly remarked out loud, "You're fat, you have to lose some weight." My daughter, who was 20 years old at the time, overheard me and said, "That's a terrible thing to say to yourself, don't say that!" I sheepishly agreed and said, "Where did you get to be so wise?" She said, "From you, and you know better!" She was right. We have to speak kindly to ourselves about ourselves. Not to mention, if we are criticizing ourselves (or others), we are criticizing God's work. *For you created my inmost being; you knit me together in my mother's womb. I praise you because I am fearfully and wonderfully made; your works are wonderful; I know that full well.*[5]

Another great place to stop sending ourselves negative messages is when we overeat or skip a workout. I am not saying to overeat and skip workouts; rather, I am suggesting we look for areas to change critical self-talk to affirming self-talk. A successful concept in effective parenting is to specifically affirm that which a child does well rather than telling them what they did wrong. Saying to a child, "I really love the way you colored blue leaves on that tree" will likely result in a lot more pictures with blue-leafed trees. Affirmation feels good, and we will strive to earn more of a good thing. Notice the affirmation was specific, not general. If we just say, "that's a nice picture you drew", the child does not know anything in particular that made the picture "nice." They do not have enough information to do more of anything specific, like drawing blue-leafed trees.

We can use the same logic on ourselves. Turning this concept toward self, rather than thinking negatively about skipping a workout today, I can affirm myself for taking the stairs instead of the elevator at work. Every good choice we make is money in the bank. It cannot be undone. I took the stairs all week to my fourth-floor office, instead of the elevator.

I did this because I knew my work schedule would not allow me the time for a formal fitness class or a lunchtime run. So, I took the stairs. That's money in the bank. I cannot unwalk those steps so I can affirm that good decision. I can affirm the four days this week I chose unsweetened tea as my lunchtime beverage instead of soda. I chose soda one day and instead of focusing on that, I affirmed the unsweetened tea. Now, I want a do-over next week and my competitive nature is to beat the four-day streak with a five-day streak. This is how fitness occurs—literally one decision at a time. Affirm the good decisions and you will want more affirmation from yourself.

I make vision boards. A vision board is a graphic illustration of the things I want to accomplish—the desires of my heart in that space in time. Nearly all the images or words on my vision board come from magazine clippings, but sometimes I type or design it on my laptop and print it out. Some of my desires may seem shallow and others deep—new windows for my house, deeper relationship with God. If the desire is in my heart and I want or aspire for it, I place a representation of it on my vision board. It is not always a literal representation, sometimes it is a symbol to which I attach certain meaning. Like a picture of a Bible or journal would represent a deeper relationship with God. I have made vision boards on poster boards, through a collage of images on my cell phone cover page, a collage on a lantern in my meditation space, a cluster of images inside my credenza cabinet at work, written words on my bathroom mirror, and graphics I made and framed for my bedroom wall. Not all at once—that would be desperation! Whenever I accomplish the items on one vision board, I make another.

When I reflect on them all, I see patterns. For example, each of my vision boards include a version of Physical Wellness based on my interests: a runner (but not a racer), a person in a yoga pose, a golf course, healthy food items, couples relaxing together. Every one of the items I just mentioned, I have achieved after having placed it on my vision board, and I continue them today. I keep including them on my boards because I find more success with a visual reminder of my heart's desires. The visuals help me to counter the continual commercial images that tease me to watch marathons of my favorite reality television show; or my favorite taco chain which wants me to eat more cheesy, salty, gooeyness; or my favorite chocolate treats at the check-out counter in the pharmacy, etc. My goal is not to eradicate those guilty pleasures from my life, but to balance them with healthier choices weighting the scales heavily with the healthy. Unhealthy choices never go on my vision board; they are already prevalent in society's external environments.

As you progress through this book, you will have the opportunity to create "visions" for your own vision board or your own list of goals and aspirations. Making a physical representation of your vision is your part, then you can let God do the rest. He will not wave a magic wand and make us a particular shape or size, but He will pave the way for us to achieve our visions by giving us extra motivation, more opportunity, better resources, and sometimes He will allow hardships from which to grow into our vision. It then becomes a partnership with God where He opens doors and we have to step through them. Then more doors, and more through-stepping. We are never exempt from doing our part, and God will always give provision. For the skeptical, please know God is not playing a shell game with us; He is simply deepening our faith and drawing us closer in our walk with Him.

WE ARE IN A PARTNERSHIP WITH GOD WHERE HE OPENS DOORS AND WE HAVE TO STEP THROUGH THEM

Many people set themselves up for failure on the fitness aspect of their wellness journey because they relate fitness with formal exercise. I like formal exercise, but my husband does not—except for golf. Yet, his golf is not motivated by a desire to exercise. He uses golf for stress relief (Mental

Wellness) and socialization (Social Wellness). In place of formal exercise, my husband does yard work, home maintenance, takes the stairs instead of elevators, carries his own luggage at hotels, etc. He is very physical and it works well for him. He never runs a race, rarely rides a bike and does not go to the gym. Yet he remains fit. He does a great job pairing his personal metabolism with his interests. What I mean by that is he is physical enough in his personal daily activities to burn the calories he consumes without having to get on a treadmill. He is not a particularly big eater and his metabolism seems efficient; thus, his physical output, personal metabolism and calorie intake are balanced. Not everyone can rely just on their daily activities. We each have different physical motivation, individual metabolism and personal appetite to contend with; therefore, we each have to work with the genetic, personality and destiny DNA God gave us, and make adjustments accordingly. We can do this by adding extra activities to our daily routine, like taking a walk midday during work that includes using stairs or walking the parking garage, which has a built-in incline and works our glutes. I recently took a workday fitness walk like this with a colleague, and my wearable device "recognized" it as exercise and automatically sent it to my fitness app (they are synced) and gave me credit for those calories burned. This resulted in additional calories being added to my available calories to consume, meaning I could eat more that day if I wanted a treat or snack.

I have held a few company-wide 10K-a-day step challenges throughout my career, and employees really engaged and enjoyed them. In one particular organization, there was one group of people whom I had difficulty getting to join - our Facilities and Engineering Department. I would see them in the elevators or in the stairwells and ask them if they signed-up and invariably I would receive the same response, "I don't have time to exercise." My reply was always, "I can almost guarantee you won't have to do anything but track your steps on your phone or a wearable device and you'll find out you earn well over 10,000 steps a day." We were vying for a trophy, so I really wanted these guys and gals on our team, so we could benefit from their steps and they could benefit from the fitness and camaraderie. Somewhat selfish, I know, but win-win was my justification. They couldn't get past their presumption that fitness equals formal exercise. Yet they were already exercising. They were performing "job walks" for new building projects, taking the stairs to check lighting, carrying equipment to work on a maintenance issue. This is very important information for those who do not actually have a natural affinity for the physical dimension of wellness. People in high movement jobs such as construction, health professions, landscaping, housekeeping, highway workers, etc. can often labor less with the fitness aspect and focus more on the nutrition and sleep elements of Physical Wellness to meet their goals.

NUTRITION

Nutrition can be a tricky topic because it is filtered through millions of experts, personal experiences and lay opinions written in books, posted online, shared on social media, discussed on talk shows and provided to us by health professionals. It can seem confusing and contradictory. I once attended a great lecture by a medical doctor and nutrition expert who was a huge proponent of eating beans for health. Weeks later, my husband shared an online video from another medical doctor and nutrition expert who made a strong case that beans are the enemy. Who can we believe and where do we start? I am sorry to say I cannot offer a definitive answer on this, but there is simplification to be found in some basic scientific facts about processed foods, sugar, high saturated fat diets, overuse of salt, etc. We have to educate ourselves on the basics, so we have our own reference point for starting or maintaining good nutritional behaviors and holding ourselves accountable. Nutritional education may best be found through developing a trusting relationship with a qualified expert or health care provider with whom we have good chemistry. While we can supplement our education and nutritional counsel online or virtually, having someone who knows us and shares an interest in our well-being offers more than expert counsel; they offer social support, bringing in another very important dimension of wellness.

Each of us has a personal journey in our diet; therefore, it makes sense to customize it, using the most up-to-date information. I can only share my own customized approach for me and invite you to create your own eating plan based on your own exploration of the science of nutrition, your own DNA and your own experiences and taste buds. *The one who eats everything must not treat with contempt the one who does not, and the one who does not eat everything must not judge the one who does, for God has accepted them.*[6]

I have consistently been on the thin side and I am careful with my nutrition. Yet, I suffer from high cholesterol. It is a genetic anomaly. After another high cholesterol report from my doctor and her persistence to put me on medication to help bring it down, I asked for a three month reprieve to work on my nutrition. She agreed. Then, I planned to strip my diet even further in the direction I had already used unsuccessfully for years. What was I thinking? I could not continue the same nutrition plan and expect a different result. Then came another epiphany. I started doing research on a current diet fad. I had never gone on a fad diet before, afterall, I am a professional, right?

Through my research, I learned the diet was steeped in 20 years of successful research. Although 20 years is not really a long time, it was enough to gain my confidence. Although it was being touted as a weight loss diet, my research was on whether it could lower LDL (bad) cholesterol and raise HDL (good) cholesterol. The more I researched, the more I found that this nutrition plan might help me achieve the biometric results I was seeking. The diet was a complete departure from the nutrition I promoted and practiced, but I was convinced that a three-month trial would not hurt me. Three months later, my LDL cholesterol was 34 points less and I had dropped a pants size. It was pretty unbelievable. Although my cholesterol remains slightly above range, my doctor was convinced, with my other "in range" biometrics, that my argument against medication may be acceptable. This episode reminded me that just as Alexis's journey to weight loss came from her sense of adventure, my journey to lower cholesterol came from my willingness to depart from a norm. God has gifted us with scientific norms through the valuable research of anointed scientists and while norms are a valuable guide, God has also embedded in each of us our unique deviation from the norm!

REST

By the seventh day God had finished the work he had been doing; so on the seventh day he rested from all his work. Then God blessed the seventh day and made it holy, because on it he rested from all the work of creating that he had done.[7] Many people do not consider sleep when they think about their physical well-being, but it is part of the physical dimension. It is not only sleep that I am referring to; I am also referring to rest, or more specifically restful sleep.

Restful sleep allows the body the opportunity to recover from the day, relax the musculature and process mental and intellectual energy. It rejuvenates. When I was trying to put into words this section on restful sleep, I could not capture the essence I was seeking to impart. I journaled, prayed, meditated, then I left it alone waiting for it to come—in His timing. And it did. It came in the form of an answer to a work problem I had been pondering. I awoke one morning as I often do, thinking about God; and as I lay in bed, I reached for my phone to read my daily scripture on my Bible app. That is when He stopped me and laid it on my heart. "Affirmation," He said. It flooded my thoughts; not my original thoughts and ideas, but deeper revelations like gifts from God. The impressions continued. Yesterday in that meeting the team was talking about the new employee recognition project, the software product that could handle it, and the concept of common currency, i.e. branded apparel, gift cards, event tickets, trinkets, etc. that could be awarded to staff for good performance. Nobody brought up the value that verbal affirmation provides as recognition to an employee for a job well done. There it was. Laid right on my heart. An important concept that has to be added to the conversation on this project at work. Especially in a time when many populations are moving further away from face-to-face verbal interactions—the heart of true relationship development. An important concept, by the way, that keeps God at the heart of good leadership. A kind and genuine word to others. Affirmations.

He gave me this valuable nugget to bring to the next meeting, and He gave it to me at a time He often has in the past—after a restful night of sleep. God did not say "here is how rest is important"; rather, He gave me the actual experience of the value of rest. It refreshes us so we can function at our highest level. *But for God*, I thought, in my gratitude of His gift to me. Restful sleep affecting my Occupational Wellness by giving me a concept for this project, and the concept glorifies Him— affirmation for my brothers and sisters. I cannot tell you how many times God's ideas have made me look very good and perform very well in the workplace. Most often it is given after a restful night of sleep. He is very generous.

REST REFRESHES US SO WE CAN FUNCTION AT OUR HIGHEST LEVEL

Good rest has also often been a catalyst to answering questions I am contemplating. God uses the time to open my mind to ideas that allow me to move forward on projects that have been challenging me, or as in the previous case, to reveal something important I have left out. When I have these moments of enlightenment, I always feel they are private moments with God. Sometimes I wonder if He chooses this time to reach me because I am willful and am ever-trying to do things myself.

But it is in these quiet times upon waking that I am more surrendered, and He can do His good work in me. *In a dream, in a vision of the night, when deep sleep falls on people as they slumber in their beds.*[8]

How much sleep do we need? I am under the belief that I personally do not need a lot of sleep to achieve rejuvenation. I am disciplined about going to bed when I am tired and usually ensure I have at least a seven-hour window to sleep. However, I invariably pop open my eyes at about the five-hour mark and I am literally finished sleeping. I used to get-up and start working when I could not get back to sleep, but I traded this for using the time for prayer and reading scripture, and as previously shown, letting God fill-me-in on a few things. How much sleep a person needs is well researched and I have tried to follow the models, winding down, ceasing the use of electronics in a timely manner and allowing time to sleep. Alas, my body still regulates itself to 5-6 hours and this works for me. It is built into my DNA.

In contrast, my husband and daughter require more sleep, and rarely express the feeling of "well-rested." This variation leads me to the wonderment that restful sleep may be tied less to structure and may be tied more to one of the other dimensions of wellness for some people. Ultimately, God provides for each of us to enjoy fulfilling and rejuvenating rest, but He has customized the prescription for each of us within our DNA, sometimes outside of scientific norms. Thus, restful sleep comes easy for me and is a place after which God meets me. For my husband and daughter, God may be waiting for them in another place that will lead them to restful sleep. What I know for certain is God wants rest for us all. *Come to me, all you who are weary and burdened, and I will give you rest. Take my yoke upon you and learn from me, for I am gentle and humble in heart, and you will find rest for your souls. For my yoke is easy and my burden is light.*[9]

YOUR WELL WITH GOD JOURNEY

As I alluded to in Chapter One, the three-in-one nature of Physical Wellness—fitness, nutrition and sleep—makes it a proverbial triple threat and can be an excellent catalyst for success in the other areas. Our goal in this journey is to identify strengths from which to build. Take a moment and ask yourself what part of the Physical Wellness dimension resonated with you most. What are you still thinking about from the fitness, nutrition and sleep discussions? Jot down a few things to think about later, meditate or pray on, and consider adding to your vision board.

ENDNOTES

1. Isaiah 64:8, NIV.
2. Psalm 37:4, NIV.
3. Psalm 20:4, NIV.
4. Romans 12:1, NIV.
5. Psalm 139:13-14, NIV.
6. Romans 14:3, NIV.
7. Genesis 2:2-3, NIV.
8. Job 33:15, NIV.
9. Matthew 11:23-30, NIV.

Chapter 3

FINANCIAL WELLNESS

*"Your life does not get better by chance,
it gets better by change."*

–JIM ROHN

Another powerhouse of the WELL WITH GOD model is Financial Wellness. Financial Wellness is not as much about the size of our bank account as it is about the quality of our financial habits, our attitude, and our perspective about money. Like Physical Wellness it can often be outwardly recognized by others and invite positive benefits in the way people respond to us. While physical well-being may prompt compliments and admiration, financial well-being often attracts respect from others. Right or wrong, the visible attributes of a person who is financially or physically well attract certain behaviors from others because they are often outwardly visible in the person's behavior and their personal presentation. I am not talking about people who are showing-off by blinging or preening. Those things may show physical and financial success, but they do not necessarily indicate *wellness*, because wellness is grounded in God; and people who are grounded in God lead with their love and their heart, not with their "things" or physical presence.

I make this point to emphasize that there are certain dimensions of wellness that more outwardly project themselves to others, therefore attracting affirmation in some form; and affirmation helps strengthen other dimensions of wellness. This reinforces the concept of the interconnectedness of the dimensions, and how a domino effect occurs when one area is strengthened, causing us to operate at a higher level of wellness in other realms. Conversely, it is an important reminder that the reverse domino effect can occur when one area of well-being is lacking. Barriers can arise that make it difficult for us to achieve other dimensions, until we are generally *unwell*. All success with achieving multi-dimensional wellness begins with achieving spiritual well-being; but after that, there is no order in which we all achieve whole wellness. It begins with God and from there, the order of our journey through the dimensions will be as unique as we are, as will be the maintenance of our wellness balance.

It can be tempting to adopt or perpetuate the stereotype that one need only look good and have money and life opens up for them. This is the enemy sabotaging you. Do not listen to him. We all have the potential to be physically healthy and have good financial habits. If you reject this, you have self-created a barrier to achieving either or both. WELL WITH GOD centers on allowing God to help you find your best self. Your best self is not ugly, poor or unhealthy. Wellness is found in God first, and the rest comes. The good news is God is available and accessible to us all; therefore wellness is available to us, including Financial Wellness. Financially "well" individuals may have "things" that we notice, but they lead with their genuineness and approachable presence. They have an "it" factor and that factor is God—because while they may have possessions, they do not define themselves by their possessions, and they are not enslaved to their possessions.

To digress a moment and demonstrate that God is available to us all, I share my own experience of knowing God. I was not raised in a home that worshiped or prayed. My mother's parents were Jehovah's Witnesses, and I am not certain if she ever identified with that practice, so I think she was agnostic at best. My father was raised in the Catholic faith but was not a practicing Catholic. The only time I recall going to church was on a Christmas Eve when I was about 16 years old. My father took us to the local Catholic Church, where we had never been before; but we left church early because the priest talked about tithing, which upset my father. I think I learned a dinnertime and bedtime prayer from my father, but generally, we did not pray together as a family and we did not attend church. So how did I know to pray? How did I develop a belief in God? Why did I always feel connected to Him and turn to Him when I was troubled? Parts of my early spiritual beliefs came from my external environment—television, books, school, neighbors, friends, relatives, etc. Yet, I felt God's presence deep inside me and this had nothing to do with my environment. I was often troubled due to home-life issues, which bled into social life issues, and I always turned to God for help. How did I know to do that? It would not be until I was an adult and explored religion on my own, that I would label this *knowing* as the Holy Spirit. This is how I know God is available to us all. I was not special, yet I am special. We are *all* special. Do not let the enemy pit us against others because of their wellness with God and all He abundantly has opened up for them. And certainly, do not let the enemy pit us against ourselves with negative talk about what we can or cannot achieve in our wellness journey. We can all achieve financial well-being, yet this does not mean we will all become millionaires. As I said, Financial Wellness is not necessarily about the size of our bank account.

A DEEP DIVE INTO FINANCIAL WELLNESS

Financial Wellness is the concept of viewing money from a health perspective, examining traditional beliefs about it, and how God expects us to view and handle money. We can elevate our experience with money by expanding our understanding about our own behavior and feelings around money and wealth and how it affects, or infects, the other dimensions of wellness, including our emotional well-being and occupational well-being. How does our attitude about money affect or infect our Financial Wellness? Although I have not explored this question with my dad, I believe it is possible that his response to the priest's comments about tithing, and his decision to gather his children and leave mass early on that Christmas Eve, may have been an infected attitude about tithing. This attitude likely derived from a bad experience with the church not helping his impoverished family during times of need, despite his mother's commitment to church attendance. Additionally, public church scandals in the media may have exacerbated my father's belief that churches use their tithed resources irresponsibly. My father would give his last dollar to any family member or friend in need; but I am quite certain he would never give it to a church, and probably not to any organized charity.

Most of us struggle in the area of Financial Wellness at some point in our lives, and many have known nothing *but* struggle when it comes to finances. To find well-being in our finances, we need to examine our individual concept of wealth, develop a healthy respect for money, lay down fears about having or not having money, and follow God's lead in how we can handle and feel about our own personal wealth. *A good name is more desirable than great riches; to be esteemed is better than silver or gold.*[1]

A 2014 Harris Poll survey, on behalf of the American Psychological Association, indicated that 72% of 3,068 American adults surveyed reported feeling stressed about money within the 30 days prior to the survey. In short, 72% of people feel financial stress, recently. *Not 72% have felt* stress at some point in our lives. Right now, today, this month, 72% of us—me, you, colleagues and family members, strangers and acquaintances are financially stressed. Seventy-two percent!

For many of us, ambition to earn or otherwise obtain greater amounts of money is tied to the desire to unburden ourselves from financial stress. Therefore, I emphasize the concept that money is not necessarily about its face value but perhaps more about how we feel with money in our lives—less stressed, in-control, more important, accomplished, powerful, etc. Some of these emotions have more noble stirrings and others do not. Then, we are presented with an additional question: if we earn more, do we use it toward lowering our stress and feeling more in control? Do we use our additional earnings to lower our debt or more easily manage our daily living expenses; or do we use it to buy more and gain more expensive taste, resulting in the same level of stress? If we become more powerful, do we use it to elevate our ego or to honor our God?

If money has a value greater than its face-value and we can use it to reduce stress and increase our feelings of control, importance, accomplishment and power, then by keeping our attitude and behavior rooted in God we can achieve financial well-being instead of just accumulating dollars and debt. Money is actually a tool through which we can exercise faith, discipline, sacrifice and generosity. If we can replace the stress, insecurity, greed and other negative emotions we have around finances, and look at the character-building opportunities it creates, we are presented with yet another amazing way to connect with God. *The Lord will open the heavens, the storehouse of his bounty, to send rain on your land in season and to bless all the work of your hands. You will lend to many nations but will borrow from none.*[2]

I want to introduce the concept of viewing money as a responsibility, not as a physical, tangible item. When I say to view it as a *responsibility*, I am not saying view it as a burden or work. Sometimes the word responsibility has heaviness attached to it because it feels obligatory and laborious. I want to offer a different perception of what having a sense of responsibility means. An important thing to recognize about responsibility is, if we are able to identify an area of responsibility, we have *vision*. Someone without vision sees no area of responsibility. If we are able to identify an area of responsibility, we are thinking bigger than ourselves. If we are responsible, we are unlikely to be selfish and egocentric. If we are able to identify an area of responsibility, we are problem solvers, because identifying responsibility is the precursor to taking action. Therefore, we can view our aptitude for recognizing responsibility as a blessing, rather than an obligation. If you fall into this category, congratulations! Give yourself credit and affirmation! This is a first step toward Financial Wellness, and the next domino that will fall into place behind it—Mental Wellness.

What if we have a low-level aptitude for recognizing responsibility? In this case, our first step is self-exploration to learn if this is a good thing or a bad thing in our life, starting with the question, do I truly *not* recognize responsibility or have I actually recognized it and intellectually jumped ahead to the next step, which is: Where there is responsibility, action is required. Remember, taking no action is an action. In this case, our obstacle is not recognizing responsibility, it is our behavior around taking subsequent action. This may be where the negative heaviness of obligation comes into play for many because an action implies "this or that." At this point, we can visualize the proverbial devil on one shoulder and the angel on the other. If you are starting to relate to this perspective on responsibility, make sure you affirm yourself for the fact that you actually *do* have vision. Congratulations! Now you have to explore the piece about *taking action* and may have a little work to do in that area.

Financial responsibility puts us in the position of making *this* or *that* choices. Heavy choices. "Do I buy formula for the baby or do I pay the electric bill?" Light choices. "Do I get new running shoes or a new accessory for my truck?" Practical and impractical choices. "Do I pay the phone bill with this paycheck or do I buy tickets to the concert so I can go with my friends?" Short-term versus long-term choices. "Do I increase my education to lead to a higher paying job in the future or do I get out there and start making money to pay for my current bills?" Life altering choices. "Do I set-aside my passion for now or do I have unprotected sex that may result in the care of a child with someone to whom I am not committed?" Selfless choices: "Do I tithe, do I tip, how much and how often?"

Each of these examples includes a sacrificial choice. Sacrifice may conjure images of doing without, but if we are rooted in God, sacrifice is tied to adding to ourselves by building our character. Sacrifice requires discipline. Discipline is required to follow God's will for us. The example of baby formula versus the electric bill is the most challenging of all the instances above. Yet, it allows us the greatest immediate route to relying on God. Feeding the baby is an obvious priority, allowing or requiring faith that we will find a community resource to help with the electric bill or allowing a family member or acquaintance the blessing of helping us in our time of need. In this case, the sacrifice and faith of a mother, begets the sacrifice and compassion of another. God is in the midst of these moments. He is with the mother in her sacrifice strengthening her through the difficult choice and promising to bless her for her faithfulness and commitment to her first priority. He is with the giver for making their own sacrifice and showing compassion through action. *And do not forget to do good and to share with others, for with such sacrifices God is pleased.*[3]

What if we choose not to sacrifice but to decide on both *this* and *that*, from some of the other examples above, acquiring debt as an option to make the decision. The problem with this is we do not get to grow our character of discipline by making sacrifices. Rather, we may be actually nurturing our selfish nature and feed a pattern that is not aligned with financial well-being. I want to take a moment here to acknowledge that sacrifice is not meant to imply suffering. We can look at making sacrifices as prevention. We make small sacrifices along the way in an effort to reduce our burden of suffering later. We can choose acquiring debt in order to satisfy our desire for both *this* and *that*, which ultimately results in our "suffering" the consequences of a new credit card bill in about 30 days. If we do this several times, we can easily grow surmounting debt, causing greater suffering, whereas if we had made a minor sacrifice initially, we would have avoided suffering later.

What we would have is a reinforced view that our sacrifice did not hurt so bad, and we strengthen our character through achieving a step toward greater financial discipline. Do we have more money in our pocket at this point? No, but we do not have less, which would have been the result if we accepted the debt option to satisfy desire to choose *both* over *this* or *that*. This is why I stated earlier that Financial Wellness is not about having large sums of money. It is about having healthy behaviors and attitudes.

FINANCIAL WELLNESS IS NOT ABOUT HAVING LARGE SUMS OF MONEY. IT'S ABOUT HAVING HEALTHY BEHAVIORS AND ATTITUDES

I want to say a word about something of which I have little experiential knowledge—earning large sums of money and taking risks with it. I recognize the previous discussion about Financial Wellness may speak loudly to those who are trying to get their finances organized or under control, which is not necessarily a time to be taking risks with money. However, there are some who aspire to earn large amounts of money and take risks with money and it turns out very well for them. Does the spirit in which they earn and risk their money matter? Does it matter to God? I believe so. I believe it can be tied to their God-given heart's desire and planned destiny.

Having abundant finances is not a negative thing. Having adequate and abundant financial resources, while grounded in God, opens the door to less stress, daily feelings of stability, hope for a future, opportunities to give to others above and beyond the general tithe, and opportunities to engage in activities tied to your heart's desire, such as educational opportunities, adventure, traveling, etc. Just as one person may be blessed and easily motivated in the physical dimension of wellness, another can be blessed with financial acumen that makes abundant finances come easily.

Aaron has an impressive mind when it comes to strategy with money. He is formally trained in accounting and has a great accounting mind. He uses it like a chess game, naturally, always strategizing "if this, then that" scenarios. I have never known anyone like him before in person, and I do not have his gifts, yet I love to hear him talk about these things. I learn from him. Aaron came from humble and modest beginnings and used his "if this, then that" gift to commit to taking out student loans for college, first one, then two then three. *If I take on this debt now, then I can get xyz job and pay the debt off by xyz, and I have greater opportunities to fulfill my career goals and live a lifestyle to which I aspire.* I relate to this because it was my same mentality and it paid off. Not as lucratively, because my gifts and ambition are in a less lucrative field of work, yet I also experience financial and occupational well-being. Remember, we can all achieve Financial Wellness, yet this does not mean we will all become millionaires. My aspirations were not about aspiring for wealth, but aspiring for health. They can both be ok, particularly when grounded in God.

Aaron earned his advanced degrees in fields of study that utilizes his strengths, which led to a high paying job with the potential to earning even higher future pay. He began paying-off his student loans as a priority and then used his understanding of accounting to look at *all* the possibilities available to him with his surplus income. Unlike me, who looks down the road to longevity—5 years, 10-20 years and retirement. Aaron looks more broadly in the *now*, in addition to longevity and retirement. Yet I do not sense greed in his spirit. Rather, I sense boundlessness in the possibilities. I think he is gifted naturally in understanding higher level behaviors around money, and he allows himself to use those gifts. Aaron is not only a big thinker, he is generous. I do not believe he currently belongs to a church, but I know he was raised in a Christian home, attended church, and has a deep and abiding faith in God. I know he gives to charitable causes, donates his time charitably, and is a very good tipper. He is also a great gift giver, focusing not on the brand of a gift, but its value to the receiver—a special National Geographic toy for an aspiring scientist, trendy new exercise equipment for a fitness junkie, a charm for a loved one's charm bracelet, etc. Aaron's broad thinking extends to the community by investing in community growth through real estate to create affordable housing opportunities for multiple income levels. While his choices are also strategic in that they are designed to put additional money in his pocket, his focus is on projects that fulfill a need in the community. I have seen him in situations in which others may get hostile or agitated, yet he remains calm, resolution-focused, and always takes the road that leads to all parties being respected with their dignity intact at the end of the situation. Aaron has that "it" factor I talked about. Not surprisingly, his overall wellness status is high. He has experienced the domino effect at an early age and continues to nurture the many dimensions of wellness, maintaining and growing his well-being. Aaron is God-centered, listening closely to the inner voice of God and following it with discipline.

Key components of financial well-being are demonstrated personally by having a budget and exercising discipline with the budget. It is evident in our priorities with our money. It is evident in our planning in-the-now around expected and unexpected expenses and our preparedness for the future. *The plans of the diligent lead to profit as surely as haste leads to poverty.*[4] My husband, Dan, and I had a small, yet significant financial windfall for the first time in our lives when we sold a house. We nearly doubled our investment. I wanted to spend the extra cash excessively, but we sat down and made a plan. First, we gave a tidy sum to the couple across the street from our property who had helped maintain the house and yard for house showings, since we no longer lived full-time in the state. They helped us for over a year with no expectation of any remuneration. They were an unbelievable blessing in many ways. We wanted to show our gratitude by giving them a substantial stipend for their kindness. We also tithed to our church, we gave some money to our daughter to help with her student loans, and we invested in a small project on our new home that added value. Our biggest purchase was a new wedding ring to replace the one I had lost nine years earlier. I was ecstatic, as I had been wearing a fashion ring Dan bought me during an overseas trip when he was in the US Navy. At the time of the loss, I could not settle on a reasonable replacement for my lost wedding set due to its sentimental value. Dan bought my wedding ring when we were poor college students, then added to it 10 years later, and when my mother passed away, we incorporated her solitaire into my wedding set. It was not elaborate, but it was special and held sentimental value. After losing my wedding ring, I wore the fashion ring for nine years and was satisfied; but then the setting kept falling out, and I kept taking it to the jeweler to no avail. I needed to replace it, but did not have a plan. Our thirtieth anniversary was coming up, and we had surplus from our home sale, so Dan told me he had "something in mind." He worked with a jeweler friend to purchase my thirtieth wedding anniversary ring, which was very much welcomed and appreciated. We still had surplus from our home sale so we left it in the bank "just in case."

Just in case came a few months later when my husband's company was purchased by another one and the new company fortunately retained him but moved him four hours from our home and my work. I stayed back to continue working, to sell our "new" house, and to look for a job in the new city while holding down my existing job. This led to an 18 month attempt to sell the "new" house and a discovery that it needed substantial structural work as a result of shoddy construction in order to sell … at a loss. Both of those factors wiped out the extra cash we had from the previous home sale. We were not happy about this situation, and our mantra started to be a bitter commentary; but we immediately recognized that if we let the enemy work a negative narrative in our minds, we would carry it into all aspects of our lives. Instead, we told ourselves, "It's God's money anyway." We reminded ourselves we were fortunate that He blessed us with a lucrative sale two years earlier in another state, so we could have the money to sustain these financial setbacks with minimal impact on our everyday living budget. We were blessed that Dan didn't get laid off, but was transferred. It was not always easy, but we kept our eyes on the blessing rather than the money, or loss of money. When it was all said and done, the house sold and closed 10 days before a major hurricane devastated the city, leaving the house unscathed but further devalued in a devastated real estate market. This is when we lost all doubt that God had our backs. Some may ask, "If He had your back, why did you have to go through all of that in the first place?" Or, "Why were you blessed and others' homes flooded?" The answer lies in knowing *all* things, even negative things, are opportunities for us to remain grounded and faithful to God, which prepares us to accept greater gifts in our personal character and greater opportunities for success in our lives. This was part of our journey to understanding *our* personal Financial Wellness, and it prepared us for what was yet to come. We trust and know God was also working in the lives of others who had different challenges than ours during this devastating natural disaster.

Three years later, Dan *was* laid off and we lost over half of our household income in one afternoon. Literally seconds after we let that sink in, we both said, "God's got this. He has a plan for Dan." We were actually optimistic because the company was very disorganized and unstable. It was a weird relief. They were lucky to have him for the period they did, and now God had another plan. We recalculated our budget, tightened our spending, continued to tithe, and were able to move forward with greater faith and an excited expectancy of "what blessings does God have planned for us?" You may wonder how we did not get scared and frantic. It was because we had money, but money did not "have" us. We were good stewards of the money God blessed us with. We were disciplined in the abundant times, as well as the lean times. This was but a season, and in the grand scheme of life, we had God and each other, and cutting back on luxuries was not difficult.

THE BLESSINGS OF TITHING

I would like to shift the Financial Wellness discussion to a discussion about tithing. A couple of years ago, I was attending our previous church for a Wednesday night service. It was a mega church, very different from the type of church we attended and raised our daughter in for years. I really enjoyed the services. During the collection of tithes this particular evening, I turned to my left to take the bucket from the gentleman next to me. He was a large, burly man, kind of disheveled, and was dressed like he had come to church after a hard day laboring outside on a job. I turned to take the bucket just in time to see him nonchalantly place several hundred dollar bills in as an offering. I was surprised because he was not dressed like a person who would have several hundred dollars in his pocket, let alone have that much money to easily give away. I, on the other hand, was in my business suit and designer high heels, and I took the bucket and passed it on without placing anything inside. I was embarrassed, but not because I did not tithe. I had tithed. We gave online at the beginning of each month. I was embarrassed about my judgment of the brother-in-Christ who sat next to me, based on his appearance. I can only imagine what he may have thought of me! Perhaps he was the better man, and thought nothing at all. I like this possibility.

We are believers in tithing to the church. Our family used to be obligatory tithers, remaining suspect of the whole "racket." Then Dan and I heard the Word of God interpreted in a way that made sense to us, and we joined a church where we can see the amazing work our church and her leaders are doing in the community, in our country, and in the world. We now feel blessed to be a part of that, and to be in a position to give. It is because of this progression of our faith that Dan and I are also able to recognize that "It's God's money anyway." We are faithful givers, we are cheerful givers, but I will confess we weren't always. Dan and I started tithing back in the day when people put cash in the offering tray, then it became a weekly check, then a monthly check mailed in an envelope. The monthly envelope that we mailed gave us angst because everyone in the pew would not "see" us giving each week to confirm our piety. Now we give online in a monthly debit from our checking account, and we have had to practice and become more grounded in the virtue of giving in privacy with God as the knower of our gifts rather than others. This places God again at the heart of our financial decisions. We don't give to receive but we do receive because we give. We receive the blessings of being able to help others near and far, we receive gratitude in our hearts that we are in a position to give, we receive the blessings that God pours out on us because we are faithful and trusting. If you do not believe this, I challenge you to try it for a year and I feel certain you will experience two things in return: A deep satisfaction in your generosity not previously experienced and additional blessings returned to you from God for your faithfulness. I believe tithing is transformational.

Much has been said and many interpretations have been given for the scripture from Matthew: *Again I tell you, it is easier for a camel to go through the eye of a needle than for someone who is rich to enter the kingdom of God.* [5] Once, after I proudly posted a photo of myself at our new church, I was replied to by a person from my hometown high school, whom I had not seen or spoken to in at least 30 years. He wrote the Matthew 19:24 scripture and used it to criticize my pastor, who also happens to be successful and world renowned—and very wealthy. I was immediately offended, but rather than retort, I simply hit "unfriend." I didn't want his battle with the enemy to infect my peace. I decided a long time ago, I practice tolerance and evolve my compassion as a human being everyday through many mediums, especially my prayer and spiritual life. My social media account is a place for posts about family, kittens, calls for assistance and inspiration—not my place for dialogue about heady subjects and definitely not a place where I have to defend where and with whom I choose to tithe, worship and praise God.

My pastor's messages offer me an interpretation of God's word that frees me from judgment of others and myself. He has been the vessel through which my transformation into a better person has occurred. Because of this pastor and this church, I have read the Bible for the first time in my life and have made positive changes that others have noticed and commented on. I did not start tithing at this church because he guilted me into giving a donation. We were always tithers; however, the attitude and gratitude with which we tithe has blossomed. No expectancy, just giving. Yet, blessings abound. Because of clear messages in the Bible about how God wants to bless us, I am certain that financial blessings are part of His plan and that the emphasis should be, not on the financial abundance, but on how we view, handle and behave with finances. As I said previously, we can *have* money but money cannot *have* us.

WE CAN *HAVE* MONEY BUT MONEY CANNOT *HAVE* US

YOUR WELL WITH GOD JOURNEY

I believe and have experienced personally that when exercised in the spirit of faith, discipline, sacrifice and generosity, we can all become financially WELL WITH GOD. *God said to Solomon, "Since this is your heart's desire and you have not asked for wealth, possessions or honor, nor for the death of your enemies, and since you have not asked for a long life but for wisdom and knowledge to govern my people over whom I made you king, therefore wisdom and knowledge will be given you. And I will also give you wealth, possessions and honor, such as no king who was before you ever had and none after you will have."[6]*

Financial well-being is a transformational catalyst for success in other dimensions of wellness. Take a moment and ask yourself what part of the Financial Wellness dimension resonated with you most. What are you still thinking about? Jot down a few things to think about later, meditate or pray on, and consider adding to your vision board.

ENDNOTES

1. Proverbs 22:1, NIV.

2. Deuteronomy 28:12, NIV.

3. Hebrews 13:16, NIV.

4. Proverbs 21:5, NIV.

5. Matthew 19:24, NIV.

6. 2 Chronicles 1:11-12, NIV.

MENTAL WELLNESS

"Whatever you hold in your mind on a consistent basis is exactly what you will experience in your life."

–ANTHONY ROBBINS

During Easter break from college in 1981, approximately one month before my twentieth birthday, I decided to end my life. Nobody expected this from me. I was popular, attractive, outgoing, majoring in broadcasting in college and getting "air time" with the campus radio news, and even landed an upcoming radio show. I had a fun job on campus, I exercised, ate healthy food, did not overindulge in alcohol and did not take drugs. Other than a recent boyfriend break-up, everything looked great from the outside. I had always been a very sensitive person, but sensitivity had progressed to a severe and dark depression, and I had been on a roller coaster of ups and deep downs for a couple of years, especially when I left for college. Literally one year earlier, I had a serious bout of anxiety and depression and called my dad from my dorm, a desperate and crying mess. Jumping into action, my dad contacted a somewhat random professor at my school and asked him to put me on a bus home, which he did - that day. I spent that summer in outpatient counseling, during one of my "up" periods, telling the psychiatrist about all my activities, successes, social life, etc. He was completely satisfied and convinced that I was a well-adjusted young woman, who would continue on the path to success now that therapy had come to an end, and the new semester was ready to start. Now a year later, I was in worse mental shape than ever.

This time my help was not outpatient therapy but in-patient care where I had a most unexpected encounter with God. I was on day 18 of my inpatient hospital stay, doing my best impression of success and resiliency, even leading an exercise class for other patients in my ward. Not kidding. We had a particular group therapist who seemed irritated with me most of the time, and it finally came to a peak in a session when he called me out on the "everything is fine" character I was playing. At the time I did not understand what he was saying or doing; I just thought he was a jerk and did not "get" me. Then he said something that really ticked me off—he started talking bad about my dad. He said, "Your dad offers you the world and delivers crumbs." I was livid, but instantaneously realized I was wounded because I knew he was speaking at least partial truth. I have always been extremely close to my father. We have very similar personalities, extroverted and charismatic. Unfortunately, my father has had a lifelong struggle with alcoholism, had a very rough childhood, and battled his own demons. He was a good provider, always had wonderful intentions, and is passionate about his children; but he was out of control with his drinking for many years, which affected his behavior, and he did not become sober during my childhood, which was something I really wanted for him, from him.

In the hospital that evening, saturated with therapy and flooded with thoughts, I lay in my hospital bed sobbing quietly to myself. Although I had often sobbed and prayed to God when I was troubled, this particular evening turned-out differently. I lay curled-up in my bed, tears pouring from my eyes, asking silently for God to make my emotional pain end, as I had so many times before. I wanted to give up. I had given up before when I tried to take my life, but that was not actually giving up. It was giving into the enemy. This time I really gave up, and I gave it to God, truly. "Finally," He must have been thinking! Instantaneously, I felt this sensation, as though my stomach lining was ripping, not painfully, just ripping slowly from one end to the other. Then nothing. No more tears, no more sadness, nothing painful, nothing worrisome. Only peace.

I even had a sudden reconciliation with my father's alcoholism and recognized that that part of my childhood which previously left me feeling insecure was actually the foundation from which my inner resiliency came. In a sad way, my dad's pain became my strength. It was, in effect, a gift. I have had ups and downs, since, in my life but I have had no more misery, no more despair, no more desire to end my pain and suffering. God had led me through a dark time into lightness using an irritated and skillful psychologist, and then *He* took it from there. From this point forward, I worked through my downs with God as my strength ... and it worked ... works! *The engulfing waters threatened me, the deep surrounded me; seaweed was wrapped around my head. To the Roots of the mountains I sank down; the earth beneath barred me in forever. But you, Lord my God, brought my life up from the pit. When my life was ebbing away, I remembered you, Lord, and my prayer rose to you to your holy temple.*[1]

Three days later, I was "cured," and my group therapist no longer seemed irritated with me. I was released from the hospital ... or the insurance ran out. The truth is, the insurance *had* reached its limit and God's intervention three days earlier was perfect timing, and certainly no accident. When I finally gave up my will for His will, I received His peace in return for my despair. My peace remained and I never faced thoughts of suicide again, ever. I was fearful at times that they would resurface, but I knew intuitively that that season in my life was over. God had led me through it and I realized that I never needed to die, I did not need to end my life. I needed to *truly* begin living my life, with God, still doing my part but with God as my built-in guide. What a relief! Not alone. Immediate stress relief and immediate self-acceptance.

This was my journey from mental *un-wellness* to Mental Wellness. I left the hospital without a mental illness diagnosis, but what about those with a mental illness diagnosis? I received valuable insight from a loved one with mental illness who shared that for people who have a mental illness diagnosis, complete healing is not required to achieve mental wellness. She said that it is possible to experience the joy and peace of God while living with mental illness.

THERE IS STILL JOY IN THE MIDST OF HER DEPRESSION. THE JOY IS DIFFERENT THAN THE JOY SHE EXPERIENCES WHEN NOT DEPRESSED— BUT IT IS JOY

She can be in the midst of a depression, yet deep in the core of her soul, she retains hope and the peace of knowing that God is with her and will carry her through the depression. There is still joy in the midst of the depression. The joy is different than the joy she experiences when not depressed—but it is joy.

TOOLS FOR MENTAL WELLNESS

Every person's despair is different and as individual as their thumbprint. Yet, every person's saving grace is the same. It is God. But, Mental Wellness is not about pain and despair, rather, it is about resiliency, joyfulness, feeling uplifted and being flexible. Many of us think about Mental Wellness in terms of those times we were not mentally well. I know I do, or I would not have started this chapter with a very personal story of my lowest point in life. My reason for the story is to share the victory that came from it. I literally stand on top of that season in my life as though I have slain a dragon; because that is what I did, we did, God and me. The role I had in the victory was my willingness to discern His voice with spiritual ears and see Him with spiritual eyes and put my life in His hands. We need to have a healthy respect for the lows so we can put them into their proper place— under our feet. We do not want to put these moments behind us where we can look back at them and wonder if they will sneak-up on us, again. We want to put them under our feet like the serpent they are and exercise the God-strength and victory within us. *Therefore put on the full armor of God, so that when the day of evil comes, you may be able to stand your ground, and after you have done everything, to stand.*[2]

The best way I know to present the path to Mental Wellness is to provide some fairly structured information and then provide some skills that can help bring us back into well-being when the enemy is luring us away. Probably the most succinct definition I have read describing the difference between mental health and emotional health is from WebMD author Andrea Herron (WebMD Health Services, Well-Being Trends, The Emotional and Mental Aspects of Well-being, July 12, 2017). Herron wrote, *Mental health refers to your ability to process information. Emotional health, on the other hand, refers to your ability to express feelings which are based upon the information you have processed.* Here is where I add to the topic to arrive at Mental Wellness. I include the popular concept of emotional intelligence, first coined by Michael Beldoch in the 1960s and later enhanced by Daniel Goleman in the 1990s. Emotional Intelligence basically uses the elements of mental and emotional health as described above to guide thinking and behavior, and our ability to manage or adjust emotions so we may adapt to environments. These descriptions are very simplistic and rudimentary explanations of more complex science, but for our purpose here, they serve as basic guidance and a starting place for understanding how to start a journey toward Mental Wellness. Put simply:

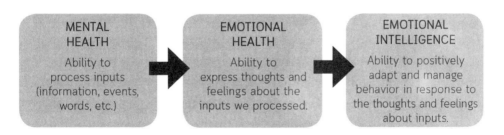

In the above illustration, I present to you my definition of Mental Wellness, the second triple threat (Physical was first) and the third dimension that I consider to be a powerhouse in the WELL WITH GOD model (Physical and Financial were #1 and #2). This dimension of wellness can have such a strong domino effect that there was a time I considered putting it at the core of the model. That is, until God nudged me! I came to believe it is more important for Mental Wellness to have a regular seat at the table, making it much less scary and recognizing that God is truly at the center of our health and well-being.

I feel confident the difference between those of us who achieve consistent feelings of mental well-being and those of us who do not, lies in our ability to successfully transition through each part and end with successfully achieving emotional intelligence:

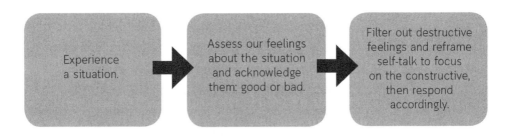

This is not about denial of the negative, rather it is the separation of good and evil. We need to experience all our emotions, even the negative ones; But, we do not want to stay there. We *can* focus on the negative, which the enemy would love us to do, because he loves to deliver misery to people. Or, we can focus on the positive, even if it means getting creative to see the positive. After my epiphany in that hospital room, I could have chosen to dwell on the shortcomings of my family life, which would have kept me on the cycle of despair, bitterness and defeat. That was the path I had previously taken. This time, I surrendered to God and asked Him for peace, and peace He gave me. It was not enough to surrender intellectually, by saying it in my head and hoping it happened. I had done that many times before, and although God sustained me, He wanted me closer. He wants us all close. To get close we have to surrender spiritually to Him, not our idea of Him. One of my favorite lessons from a pastor at a previous church, is this:

QUESTION: *How does God speak to us?*

ANSWER: *He lays it on your heart like a whisper.*

QUESTION: *Why does He whisper?*

ANSWER: *Because He is close.*

> *The Lord said, "Go out and stand on the mountain in the*
> *presence of the Lord, for the Lord is about to pass by." Then a*
> *great and powerful wind tore the mountains apart and shattered*
> *the rocks before the Lord, but the Lord was not in the wind.*
> *After the wind there was an earthquake, but the Lord was not in*
> *the earthquake. After the earthquake came a fire, but the Lord*
> *was not in the fire. And after the fire came a gentle whisper.*
> 1 KINGS 19:11-12 NIV

In the previous illustration, I introduced reframing self-talk. This is a key skill in managing and achieving a high level of Mental Wellness. Self-talk is the conversation we create in our head, and it is driven by our view or perspective of a given situation. Our view, or perspective, is influenced by our Locus of Control (LOC). Everyone has a LOC, either internal or external. Those who operate from an internal LOC are of the belief that what they get out of life has a lot to do with their own efforts. Those who operate from an external LOC are of the belief that outside influences such as luck, fate, karma, etc. are mostly the determinants of how life turns out for them. Where is God in either of these descriptions? In the science of LOC, God is not discussed. Yet, God is most assuredly present in the model. It may be a surprise to you that God is found in the internal Locus of Control because God is *in* us, and we meet and experience God internally. Remember, He is close. If we are externally controlled we put Him on the outside in the company of luck, fate and Karma, which is not a *Master*-planned community! This is not where God belongs. He works through us, from the inside.

If we recognize we are operating from an External LOC, there is good news! We can redirect ourselves to the internal realm through a concept called Cognitive Restructuring. Cognitive, meaning we make a conscious, thoughtful choice to do something. That something is re-frame, or restructure, our "self-talk" from negative thoughts or feelings to positive ones. Considering the previous illustrations, Emotional Intelligence is related to our ability to adapt and manage our behavior in response to the thoughts and feelings about inputs. This is the pivotal moment when we decide whether we will *react* or *respond* to the situation. Responding requires thought, so if we are not thinking and we are just taking action, speaking or behaving spontaneously, this is reacting and this is not going to move us in the direction of high-level mental well-being.

If we are a quick study and can immediately restructure our self-talk on demand when it happens, Bravo! However, most of us have a learning curve and have to train ourselves to respond instead of react. This can take time. We know we are progressing in the right direction when the time frame between reaction and realization decreases. For example, I may react to a situation and the next day I may think, "I should have handled that differently." Soon, I may notice it a few hours after the reaction, followed by noticing it minutes afterward the next time. Then, I make a big leap to noticing during the reaction and can re-frame it before I go into full reaction mode.

The peace comes when I experience the trigger and before I react, I stop and think about it, even pray about it, and determine what is the best way to view and feel about the situation, so that I see it as a blessing or opportunity, instead of as an inconvenience or problem. If

I do it right, I will soon stand on top of the problem as a victor, and I will be more able to do the same next time, and again and again. Any trigger God allows the enemy to put in our path, He has provided a way through that brings us out on top. *No temptation has overtaken you except what is common to mankind. And God is faithful; he will not let you be tempted beyond what you can bear. But when you are tempted, he will also provide a way out so that you can endure it.*[3]

An additional benefit to viewing our lows as a blessing is that it breeds understanding for others when we recognize them going through challenging seasons in their mental health. Thus, it serves as a call-to-action in how we treat others out of consideration for their state of mind. This, in turn, transforms us into a role model for others to follow. See how great our times of darkness and defeat are? God makes them available to us, if we will let Him, so we may grow exponentially to help, not only ourselves, but to help others. *Do not conform to the pattern of this world, but be transformed by the renewing of your mind. Then you will be able to test and approve what God's will is -his good, pleasing and perfect will.*[4]

Yet the most vital reason to let our lows be a blessing is self-acceptance. Self-acceptance is at the core of Mental Wellness, but can be hard to come by for many of us. We may have feelings of shame, worthlessness, low self-esteem, and guilt. This is the devil's playground and the place where we have to practice, then master, Cognitive Restructuring.

One of the first places we start to see self-acceptance is often in our ability to laugh at our own mistakes. Later, we may dabble in self-deprecating humor; but we must be very careful with this, because it can become a mask, and easily turn into self-criticism, negative self-talk and can send the message that others may take cheap shots at us as well. Not good. Self-deprecation is a passive-aggressive communication style and passive-aggressive communication is low in respect when used toward anyone, including ourselves. Let us stick with good, old fashioned self-acceptance, sharing our stories of overcoming obstacles when and where appropriate, and leave out the self-deprecation. It becomes infectious.

In the discussion of responding vs. reacting, I mentioned the word "trigger." What I am specifically referring to is a "stressor." Stressors are the catalysts for stress. There are positive stressors—a marriage, birth of a baby, a promotion at work. There are negative stressors —a break-up, a sick child, getting laid off from work. There are long term stressors— cancer treatment, long term debt repayment, weight loss plan. There are short term stressors—a near miss in traffic, a power surge while working on our computer, a broken appliance at home. Our body responds physically and mentally to stress, but we can affect the intensity and duration of our physical and mental response, based on how we choose to view it. So stressors are our pivot points for Cognitive Restructuring.

I told the story in Chapter One about praying for God's help with a disagreeable co-worker and God *told* me to write this book. There is more to this story. As you know, I started writing the book and submitted the proposal to the literary agent who expressed interest. Then, nothing. I waited. *Enter stressor.* After an appropriate wait, I reached out to the agent and was asked to wait a couple more weeks because the agency had not yet reviewed my proposal. More waiting. The enemy started to tell me I was crazy for thinking I could write a book, or that it would be good enough for anyone to publish or read. I was struggling with putting the success of this book in the hands of the agent, and was starting to operate from an external LOC, even though I was talking to God and praying to Him about it as though I was operating internally. I knew I was operating externally because I was not at peace, I was "at stress."

My thoughts started to fixate on "what if" scenarios. Still operating externally, I shared my plight with a pastor who put it simply: "God did not tell you to publish a book, He told you to write it." To which I replied, "Ahh. I guess I'd better get started on Chapter Two!" I shifted to an internal LOC, and I stopped stressing-out about *what next,* and returned to focus on *what now*. Here I returned to my peace. Now, I use my vision board for the *what next*, and I keep myself focused on the *what now*.

Stressors, self-talk, and cognitive restructuring represent predominant elements in achieving a high state of Mental Wellness. Now, I want to shift the conversation to medication, drugs and alcohol. This will be brief because I am not a clinician, and this is sensitive, serious territory that I am not qualified to discuss clinically. Therefore, I will stick to my professional experiential and spiritual perspective. We live in a culture where mental health medications (meds) are used routinely. I am a true believer that mental health meds can be valuable, even invaluable, at times. Still, while we are in those seasons when we are relying on our healthcare provider and medication, keep in mind that this occurs in the realm of external LOC, in that we are putting our care in the hands of professionals and sometimes medication. At the same time, we must also work to keep our foot-in-the-door of internal LOC by learning to help ourselves and by working with a qualified mental health counselor and/or pastoral counselor. Most importantly, however, we must trust in God to sustain and strengthen us, through these valuable resources he has provided (doctors, medication, counselors), through resiliency that He has blessed us with, and also through supernatural healing that only He can offer. We do not have to wait until we are in our darkest hour to surrender to His help, as I did in my opening story for this chapter. He wants to help every day, in every way. He even wants to hear from us in the good times, "Thank you, God, for a great day of managing my stress and resisting the urge to go off on that person." He is a faithful God—invite Him in throughout each day.

WE DO NOT HAVE TO WAIT UNTIL WE ARE IN OUR DARKEST HOUR TO SURRENDER TO GOD'S HELP

Drug and alcohol abuse is a different situation. During mental health challenges, the enemy likes to move-in like a caring and supportive friend during our vulnerability, and tempt us with the false hope of relief and even fun and happiness through drugs and alcohol. It does not work, it never has, and it never will. It is that simple. If we allow the enemy to steal our mental health through drugs and the overuse of alcohol, there is a natural fall of our Physical Wellness, Social Wellness, Occupational Wellness, and all the rest. We must be ever-vigilant when it comes to addictive substances. Keep God close, and always return to Him when we fall.

YOUR WELL WITH GOD JOURNEY

When I am feeling particularly vulnerable to the enemy's attacks on my Mental Wellness, I "put on the full armor of God," literally. It is the prayer and blessing I give myself often before I even get out of bed in the morning and it never fails me:

> *Stand firm then, with the belt of truth buckled around your waist, with the breastplate of righteousness in place, and with your feet fitted with the readiness that comes from the gospel of peace. In addition to all this, take up the shield of faith, with which you can extinguish all the flaming arrows of the evil one. Take the helmet of salvation and the sword of the Spirit, which is the word of God.*
> EPHESIANS 6:14-17, NIV

Mental Wellness rounds out the third powerhouse of the WELL WITH GOD model. Take a moment and ask yourself what part of the Mental Wellness dimension resonated with you most. What are you still thinking about? Jot down a few things to think about later, meditate or pray on, and consider adding images to your vision board that represent your future as a resilient, joyful, uplifted, and flexible person.

ENDNOTES

1. Jonah 2:5-7, NIV.

2. Ephesians 6:13, NIV.

3. 1 Corinthians 10:13, NIV.

4. Romans 12:2, NIV.

IF YOU ARE STRESSING OUT
ABOUT "WHAT'S NEXT?"
SWITCH YOUR FOCUS TO
"WHAT'S NOW?" THIS WILL
HELP YOU RETURN TO PEACE.

Chapter 5

ENVIRONMENTAL
WELLNESS

*"If we have no peace, it is because we have
forgotten that we belong to each other."*

–MOTHER TERESA

Environmental Wellness, is not about being "green," recycling, conservation, and the like. Those things are fantastic and extend into the longitudinal look at Environmental Wellness, but for the purpose of the WELL WITH GOD model, I am referring first and foremost to the quality of the environment in which we live and work from a culture perspective, not an ethnic culture, but the "vibe" we create in our home life, our work space, and our social scene. Are they congruent, and are they harmonious? Are they toxic? Are they a place we can thrive, hold healthy conversations, experience growth, be authentic, and discover our authentic self?

Achieving environmental well-being unsurprisingly occurs in predominantly drama-free settings, and it is important that we have a high level of functionality in our home life, our work/school life, and our social life if we are to maximize Environmental Wellness. If we have a work life where we are thriving but our home life is in chaos, our work/life balance gets unsettled, and depending on how we handle situations, we can easily make them mirror each other as one aspect of our life bleeds into the other. *The rain came down, the streams rose, and the winds blew and beat against the house; yet it did not fall, because it had its foundation on the rock.*[1]

TOOLS FOR ENVIRONMENTAL WELLNESS

In Chapter Four, I defined and discussed stressors and introduced the concept of restructuring or re-framing our self-talk to move it from negative to positive, basically moving it from stress-producing self-talk to stress-reducing self-talk. Now, I want to shift the self-talk to external talk, better known as our communication with others. Good communication is the single most important element necessary to create Environmental Wellness in our home, work and social environments. Being a good communicator should not be confused with being extroverted, talkative and congenial. Good communicators may talk a lot or they may talk only a little. The key ingredient is that good communicators are deliberate and thoughtful in the messages they send. They are mindful. They are responsive rather than reactive. Remember, however, the WELL WITH GOD model is not about our learning to be good, it is about our becoming exceptional. Therefore, we will look at the scientific elements of communication, then add the expectations God has for us when we communicate. Those expectations are found through exploring our goal or intention in any given exchange, and infusing respect, genuineness, time and timing. *Do not let any unwholesome talk come out of your mouths, but only what is helpful for building others up according to their needs, that it may benefit those who listen.*[2]

As a communication trainer for over 30 years, I have seen a common proclivity for readers/participants to hear the information about communication and use it to project what others should be doing to communicate better with them. This is a pitfall. This is the enemy trying to keep you from becoming your best self, and prevent you from being a servant of God. Know this: we have no ability to change another person; we only have the ability

WE HAVE NO ABILITY TO CHANGE ANOTHER PERSON; WE ONLY HAVE THE ABILITY TO CHANGE OURSELVES to change ourselves. When it comes to communication, we can learn it, master it, and model exceptional communication skills, which leads to several great outcomes: 1) Our self-confidence grows immensely, 2) Our relationships with others grow exponentially, 3) Our influence grows unexpectedly, and 4) Others may grow and rise to better communication heights as they reflect our communication skills. Now, that is God at work! Let's get started!

When I talk about communication skills, I like to set it up as a Two-Four-Six discussion. Two *parts* of communication, four *styles* of communication and six *skills* for exceptional communication. Then I add the God factors. I call them boosters!

TWO TYPES OF COMMUNICATION

- Verbal
- Non-Verbal

The two types of communication are no revelation to most people, but what I have to say about them may be. They are verbal and non-verbal communication. We all could probably have guessed those. Verbal communication represents the actual words we use. Non-verbal communication represents the "package" in which we wrap those words. Most people like to make it simple by saying non-verbal communication is body language, and then they stop there and move on. Non-verbal communication is indeed body language, but it includes far more than mere body language. Non-verbal communication is so important that it does not even require words to send a message. On their own, non-verbal messages send meaning, or invite others to determine your meaning or judge you, simply by your actions. The importance of non-verbal communication is profound, which is why it is imperative that we look at it in-depth, instead of a simple summary that non-verbal communication equates to body language.

Some research states that the non-verbal piece makes up 75% of the meaning of a message, with the words only making-up 25% of the message. Other research has non-verbal communication at 90% of the meaning of the whole message. Regardless of the ranges of percentages, we know non-verbal communication is at least 75% of the message we send; so if we want to ensure the correct message has a chance of being received, we need to ensure our non-verbals match what we say. For example, if I am saying, "I am sorry" and I roll my eyes and have a sarcastic tone, then the receiver is not likely to believe I am sorry. Or on a larger, longer term scale, if I say I am sorry, but over time I keep doing the same thing, my actions (non-verbals) are speaking louder than my words, and I am less likely to be believed. In fact, the key to building trust with anyone is ensuring the congruence of the verbal messages with the non-verbal messages we are sending to that person. If my messages are consistently congruent, then trust occurs. If not, trust is lost or is never created.

Here is the primary list of things that are included in our body language when we speak, but it is not the entirety:

1. **Tone**—sarcastic, harsh, threatening, soft and mousey, sing-songy, etc.

2. **Eyes**—eye contact, lack of eye contact, rolling, gazing, staring, shifting, glaring eyes, glazed, sleepy, piercing eyes, eyes looking past us, any type of eyes

3. **Mouth**—smile, smirk, frown, grimace, pursed lips, pressed lips, kissy lips, no smile/no frown straight lips, wide open mouth, sticking your tongue out, licking lips, smacking lips, raspberry/zurbert lips with the noise, anything involving the lips

4. **Face**—combination of eyes and mouth with the rest of the facial muscles, including eyebrows, cheeks, chin

5. **Fingers/hands/arms**—tapping, drumming, pounding, clapping, high-fiving, shaking, trembling, any gesture or lack of gesture

6. **Toes/feet/legs**—tapping, stomping, shaking, trembling, kicking, any movement or lack of movement

7. **Shoulders**—shrugging, rolling, curving, slumping, lifting, any movement or lack of movement

8. **Hips/butt**—swaying, shaking, pumping, bumping, grinding, any type of movement or lack of movement

9. **Posture**—erect, slumped, neutral, etc.

10. **Proximity**—how close we are to the person with whom we are communicating. Are we in the 18 inch personal comfort zone, outside of it, across the room, touching them, towering, etc.

11. **Status**—are we in a position of power, authority, unknown, subordinate, etc.

12. **Position**—are we seated, standing, in a corner, at the head of a table or in the center, are we at the front of a room, in the back

13. **Gait**—fast paced, limping, cocky walk, sauntering, strutting, shuffling, etc.

14. **Appearance**—skin color, clothing, hairstyle, shoes, hat, how is the hat worn, jewelry, etc.

15. **Vocal non-verbals**—talking fast, talking slow, accent, loud, quiet, stuttering, profanity, clichés, trendy terms, complex words, etc.

Think of a time you were judged solely by your actions and the person passing the judgment got it completely wrong. Now remember the part where I said we have no control over others, we only have control over ourselves. This is why it is very important to be mindful and deliberate with our non-verbals. Congruence occurs when my words match my actions. When they do, I become more believable.

Earlier in my career, I trained and practiced as a domestic mediator for the court system. In all mediation cases there are at least two parties, and these parties are in conflict over something that needs resolution. As a mediator, my job is to be a neutral third party to help the parties reach resolution. Whenever I was waiting for the parties to arrive to the designated location for the mediation, when one party arrived first, I would greet them and quickly show them to a chair or room where they could wait for the other party's arrival. Then, I would leave their presence so that when the second party arrived, I was not near or "chatting" with the first arrival. Why? Perception. The power of my presence sitting or standing with the first party who arrived can easily create a perception of camaraderie or perceived bias. We could have chatted about the weather, or the temperature of the room. It does not matter, because my proximity to the first arrival projects closeness. If I am not in the same space, then I maintain the perception I want to project—neutrality. This is how important it is to acquaint ourselves with all the subtle elements of non-verbal behavior and work to deliberately match them with our words and intentions. *A troublemaker and a villain, who goes about with a corrupt mouth, who winks maliciously with his eye, signals with his feet and motions with his fingers, who plots evil with deceit in his heart—he always stirs up conflict.*[3]

OUR NON-VERBAL BEHAVIOR NEEDS TO MATCH OUR WORDS AND INTENTIONS

FOUR STYLES OF COMMUNICATION

- Aggressive
- Passive
- Passive-Aggressive
- Assertive

There are four communication styles from which to operate. Although some of us may shift in and out of different styles, most of us have a predominant one. Caution to those who change styles for different situations and different people: This breaks the congruence and consistency rule, and trust cannot grow. I also think it begs the question, "Why do I speak some ways to certain people, but not to others?" The reality is communication is communication. It should be consistent regardless of your audience; The only thing that changes between audiences is the content. Meaning, my communication style is the same with the CEO of my company as it is with the custodial crew, as it is with husband, as it is with my daughter. Again, the content is all that changes.

The four styles are Aggressive, Passive, Passive-Aggressive and Assertive. I want to emphasize that it is easy for us to recognize these styles of communication and assign their labels to people we know, but the point in communication skills training is to keep the focus on ourselves and our own identity and assignments, because one of the best influences we have on others is our ability to be excellent communicators, which invites them to be the same.

AGGRESSIVE COMMUNICATORS

Aggressive communicators use their words and actions to try to get what they want, regardless of the impact on others. This style is characterized by verbal and non-verbal communication described by these (and many other) words: Harsh, rude, overbearing, authoritative, bullying, critical, pushy, arrogant, abusive, loud, in personal space, towering, profane, defensive, intimidating, penetrating eyes, etc. Society has often reinforced the notion of being aggressive and going after what we want. We have, in more recent years, substituted the word *aggressive* with *proactive* because we have come to acknowledge that *aggressive* is, after all, *aggressive*. It is also very low in respect to the receiver. Aggressive communicators are aggressive in both their verbal and non-verbal behavior.

If we see ourselves in some of the words or behaviors that describe Aggressive communication, our job is to remember the intersection in Mental Wellness where we use Cognitive Restructuring to keep the focus on success and not on denial or self-criticism. Make a shift and move on.

When we encounter aggressiveness in others, it is tempting to meet them there. Caution: Intersection. Do not go there. Meeting aggression with aggression keeps the situation in conflict and escalates it. If, instead, we choose assertive communication, which we will discuss last, the aggressive person has to "come-down" to meet us, and we have taken a positive step in re-routing a derailed conversation back onto the right track. This is another example of being responsive instead of reactive!

PASSIVE COMMUNICATORS

Passive communicators are the opposite of aggressive communicators. They use their communication style to let others get what they want at their own expense. Passive communication is characterized by words and behaviors such as: quiet, weak, doormat, wimpy, victim, lacking eye contact, keeping to self, no opinion, soft-spoken, etc. Passive communicators are passive in both the verbal and non-verbal aspects of their messages. Passive communication is low in self-respect.

Many people who identify with passive communication often take issue with the judgmental word list, feeling that it makes them sound weak.

An important thing to stay grounded in is the style of communication (any style) is a choice and not part of our DNA character. It is not *who* we are, it is *how* we are. Who we are is God's children. We can shift our communication style to represent Him well, bringing out the best in ourselves.

PASSIVE-AGGRESSIVE COMMUNICATORS

Passive-Aggressive communicators use their words and actions to try to get what they want indirectly. Words that characterize this style of communication include: sarcastic, deceptive, manipulative, sneaky, rolling-eyes, condescending tone, etc. Passive-Aggressive communication is known as the style of mixed messages. The words (verbals) do not match the non-verbals. When we have an interchange with someone and we walk away wondering what just happened, or our believability meter is registering low, it is usually because we are getting mixed messages. Remember, we are attributing at least 75% of the message meaning to the non verbal cues, so if we get a mixed message from someone, we are most likely believing the non-verbals over the verbals, and rightly so.

IF WE GET A MIXED MESSAGE FROM SOMEONE, WE ARE MOST LIKELY BELIEVING THE NON-VERBALS OVER THE VERBALS, AND RIGHTLY SO

I once attended a community meeting in a neighboring county, and I remarked to a county administrator that I had not yet received the application for our organization to apply for their annual grant funding opportunity. His response was vague but not negative, but his tone with me was not as warm as usual and he lacked eye contact. I returned to my office and spoke with our director and said, "I think there is going to be an issue with the grant funding from that county" (we were a regional women's shelter). I told my director why I thought this and she shrugged it off. A week later we received a letter stating the county was not going to allow any grant applicants from outside their jurisdiction, even those regional agencies serving their residents. I made that big leap, prediction if you will, based on my assessment of a subtle shift in tone and eye contact. Nothing dramatic. And I was correct. This, by the way, has also helped me assess dangerous people and dangerous situations that allowed me to avoid harm.

When we experience trust issues with others, it is invariably because they are communicating passive-aggressively. This style is also low in respect for others. Therefore, if we wish to build trusting, respectful relationships with others, we have to work on the congruence of our messages so others may have the best information they need to understand our truest intentions and meaning.

ASSERTIVE COMMUNICATORS

I have saved Assertive communication style for last because it is the catalyst for all good communication. Assertive communicators try to get what they want, while considering others and remaining flexible. Assertive communication is characterized by the following words: upfront, kind, respectful, inclusive, open-minded, frank, factual, considerate, flexible, eye contact, fluid tone. With assertiveness, both the verbal and non-verbal messages match.

Assertiveness is often confused with Aggressiveness. They are both congruent and they are both resolution-focused. To move from aggressiveness to assertiveness, we have to dial down our pushiness and add a heaping spoonful of flexibility and compromise. Some people opt for aggressiveness over assertiveness because they do not want to get "walked on." These people then turn into those who walk on others. Trust me, assertive people do not get walked on. They just use firmness, focus and flexibility to get to resolution. Still, sometimes the answer is No. Assertive people can say No; they just use more words and kinder non-verbal messages. The reason they use more words is that they explain why in an effort to provide insight, instead of a definitive, unjustified "No."

In a time when society is preoccupied with briefness, we can lose sight of the reality and value that it takes more words to communicate well. Be careful with brevity. And be careful with words alone. Emojis were created to help add the non-verbal component to our online messages, but they are inadequate, and technically they are frivolous. Good communication is not frivolous. Face-to-face, dynamic conversation is the only way to grow good communication skills and good communication, specifically assertive communication. *From the fruit of their mouth a person's stomach is filled; with the harvest of their lips they are satisfied. The tongue has the power of life and death, and those who love it will eat its fruit.*[4]

SIX SKILLS FOR ASSERTIVENESS

- "I" Statements
- Self-Disclosure
- Giving Feedback
- Receiving Feedback
- Empathy
- Listening

How do we get to Assertiveness? The path to Assertive communication is found in six skills. You will recognize some, re-label others, and hopefully add to your toolbox. It is also important to know that each skill has a goal or intention. So, use them well, not manipulatively, but decidedly, or you will find yourself in the throes of passive-aggressive communication.

"I" STATEMENTS

"I" Statements—I statements help build our sense of self, and the goal is to build rapport with the other person, share information, and demonstrate respect. *"I" statements* are not about selfishness; rather they are about owning our own thoughts, feelings, and beliefs rather than using "you" statements which assigns our thoughts, feelings, and beliefs to others. Have you ever heard someone tell a story using "you" statements as though you were the one the story is about? Did you think to yourself, "I do not feel or believe that?" Do not be that person. Speak for yourself. Own your thoughts, feelings, and beliefs by using *"I" statements.* It demonstrates respect when we speak for ourselves, and allows room for the listener to feel accepted that they may have differing thoughts, feelings, and beliefs.

SELF-DISCLOSURE

Self-disclosure—The goal of self-disclosure (SD) is to build rapport and share information; but we have to be careful not to share too much information (TMI), because TMI takes the focus off the overall message, and causes the listener to become fixated on the TMI and when it will end. Self-disclosures share information about self and require we use *"I" statements.* There are varying risk levels with self-disclosure. Low risk SDs contribute to a story, but higher risk self-disclosures can show vulnerability, and can increase the credibility level and trust for the speaker. Effective communicators choose the risk level based on what suits the conversation best. This is another example of how exceptional communicators are deliberate, with a value-added goal, not just talking to fill space. If my friend is telling me about the loss of his father and I share that I lost my mother at an early age, as well, this is a high-level self-disclosure. If instead, I share that they are the second person this week who has told me they lost a parent, this is a lower level self-disclosure and probably should have been withheld so the speaker could continue to share their experience or grief.

GIVING FEEDBACK

Giving Feedback—The goal of giving feedback (GF) is to share thoughts, feelings, and beliefs. It can have a secondary goal of inviting change or asking for something from the listener. Many of us think of GF as sharing opinion about a given topic. It is not. Most of us are familiar with this skill in a particular format. It is often presented in a formula: "When you say or do _____, I think or feel _____." People often go off-track with the fill-in-the blanks. Many put a subjective word rather than a specific descriptor. If the words are not specific, our message will be lost. Example: When you don't pay attention, I get mad. With this feedback, I know nothing about what "pay attention" or "mad" mean. A higher quality version of this example is: "When you **constantly look at your phone while I am talking to you,** I feel **not listened-to**." The difference in these two messages is clear, but let me unpack it more. In the second example, not only do I know what exactly I am doing that is a trigger or stress for the other person, I also have a greater ability to understand the speaker's feelings, because they are specific about them and they "own" their feelings. Further, I have an invitation, without being asked, to change my behavior. The speaker may add the "ask", but I recommend using the "making-the-ask" element of GF sparingly because if the speaker does not ask, and I make the behavior change on my own, I grow in my character because I made the choice, rather than I was asked, so I complied.

I have a word of caution with this skill. It can be tempting to put a "you" in the feedback formula. Do not do this. It completely takes the ownership of our own feelings out of the message and turns it into an accusation. Example: "When you constantly look at your phone while I am talking to you, I feel YOU are not listening to me." Danger, danger, accusation. In this case, we set ourselves up for an argument. Instead, try to end the sentence with an "ed" word, which almost always ensures we have used the skill correctly (not listened-to versus not listening).

All feedback does not have to be negative. It can also be positive such as, "When you put down your phone and look me in the eye when we are talking, I feel listened to." Wow! Thank you! Now the listener knows how to be a better listener and get more compliments for himself/herself. Win-win! To become an exceptional communicator, look for opportunities to affirm, rather than redirect for change.

RECEIVING FEEDBACK

Receiving Feedback (RF)—The goal of receiving feedback is to build rapport and show respect. Just because we know how to appropriately give feedback does not mean others will. Still, we can improve the level of communication by remaining skillful in receiving feedback when given, in any form. The first thing we need to do is recognize the feedback when we hear it. It may not come in a nice "package," so we have to listen for the feedback with our spiritual ears. Feedback can be "easy to hear" (positive) or "hard to hear" (negative).

Once we have recognized the feedback, we need to acknowledge it. It may be a simple "Thank you, I am glad you noticed." Or, it may be "hard to hear" feedback, and may require more than just a thank you. We can be tempted here to offer a justification or defense. Instead, I recommend offering a "next step", or the speaker may fill-in-the-blanks themselves and escalate the problem.

When my husband, Dan, and I lived in Washington State in military base housing, there were strict rules for yards, neighbors, parking, pets, etc. We had an indoor/outdoor cat which was unfortunately not allowed. One Friday, I was home alone, eight months pregnant, and heard a knock at the door. When I opened the door, our neighbor, whom I did not know but recognized, was standing in front of me. With no introduction, he blurted out, "Your cat is shitting in the planter by our front door." I did not like his delivery! However, I did recognize it as feedback, just not delivered skillfully. By this time in my career, I was an excellent communicator and was teaching communication skills to sailors on base. I knew there was feedback in that statement, and I knew just how to respond. "Okay," I said politely and neutrally, before thanking him and closing the door. In my head I was thinking, "Wow, I handled that well. I didn't go off on him or anything." I did not even feel stressed. I had resolved in my head that when my husband got home from work, I would tell him about this, and talk about what the best next step would be. I had a lot of thoughts but that is where they remained, in my head, until my husband Dan came home from work.

I told Dan the situation, sharing how proud I was that I received his feedback without becoming defensive. Dan recommended we dig out and replace the dirt, sprinkle the new dirt with a heavy dose of cayenne pepper, and the cat would not return to that area. And that is just what Dan did on our behalf due to my delicate state of impending motherhood. Dan also knocked on the neighbor's door several times to tell him our plan, but they apparently had gone out of town for the weekend. On Monday after work, Dan saw the neighbor had returned and went over, apologized for our cat, and had a polite conversation about what we did to remediate the situation. Dan is naturally an exceptional communicator. The neighbor sheepishly grimaced and told Dan that when I just said "Okay," he thought we were not going to do anything, so he contacted Navy housing and turned us in for a violation. Everything turned out fine because we remediated the issue, but I was perplexed about the failure of my Receiving Feedback skills. I realized that it is not always enough to neutrally acknowledge "hard to hear" communication; we may also need to offer a next-step, even if that next-step is, "Okay, thank you, I will speak with my husband and get back to you by the end of the weekend." Remember, it takes more words to communicate well. I failed in this case, but did not make this mistake again.

EMPATHY

Empathy—The goal of Empathy is to open dialogue between two or more people and to clarify situations. It is executed similarly to the skill of Giving Feedback, but is very different and is a most powerful tool when mastered. Empathy can also be used affirmatively, or as an agent to invite improved relationships. When used for the latter, it can also be a double-edged sword in that when directed toward very dysfunctional communicators, they often experience it as an attack. Stay focused and stay confident if this occurs. While good communication skills are meant to improve communication between two or more people, there will inevitably be those people who are not ready to evolve their relationships. It is important to be responsive, and do not let yourself be negatively affected by the enemy's work within those individuals.

As with GF, the skill of Empathy has a formula and the same rules of specificity apply, with one exception—"You" statements are allowed and are necessary. Empathy has three parts: 1). A specific observation, 2). An inference or guess about the observation, 3). Return of focus/ Check-it-out with the receiver. If you do not add the third element, you have just made an assumption, which is not skillful communication and may lead to conflict. We must always allow the other person to be the judge of their motivation, not us. While we can guess, we can be very wrong in our guesses. Here is an example of how the elements of empathy sound when put together, but remember, it is said in a fluid, flexible tone: "I asked you to slow down because it is scaring me" (#1). "You haven't slowed down and you didn't respond to me. I think you don't care about my safety or my feelings" (#2). "Is that the way you feel" (#3)? The response may be, "Not at all, I really have to go to the restroom, so I am trying to make it home quickly." Or maybe the response will be, "I'm sorry, I was thinking about work and was not listening. I'll slow down." And of course, it may open a different, yet still valuable conversation, with a response such as, "I'm only driving 10 miles over the speed limit. I won't get stopped unless I drive faster than that. Chill-out, I know how to drive a car." Regardless of the response, the opportunity for discussion, clarification, and understanding opens up when using the skill of empathy well. All answers give us valuable information, not just those answers we like to hear.

LISTENING

Listening is the last skill. The goal of listening is to understand and build respect. Listening involves not talking. It also involves paying attention to the speaker's verbal and non-verbal messages, and using our own non-verbal messages to show we are listening while suspending our words to minimalism. To be a good listener, we must stay present mentally, and not let our mind, eyes, or body language distract the speaker. We must also listen actively, in that we suspend judgment of the content, even if we disagree, or if it is a topic we have heard numerous times before. When the time comes for us to speak, it is very useful to paraphrase or summarize, so the speaker receives validation of their message, and can clear up anything we misconstrue. We may also seek clarification using the skill of empathy to answer any questions we have.

> THE GOAL OF LISTENING IS TO UNDERSTAND AND BUILD RESPECT

We have discussed the Two-Four-Six strategy for good communication. Now let's apply the boosters, the God factors: intention, respect, genuineness, and timing. To move communication from good to exceptional, we have to be rooted in God with our communication. Consider these things to help determine if you are rooted.

INTENTION/GOAL—*What is my motivation?*

- Am I adding value to the conversation?
- Am I showing off or trying to one-up the other person?
- Am I trying to "school" them?
- Am I trying to persuade them?

RESPECT

- Not judging
- Listening with my non-verbals
- Not interrupting
- Giving time to listen

GENUINENESS—*Trust is built here.*

- Congruency—do my verbals and non-verbals match?
- Consistency—must be at least 51% consistent with matching words and behavior; it is best to reach the 90%+ mark

TIMING

- Am I just trying to get my message out for my own benefit or have I considered whether the listener is in a good space mentally, location-wise, or time-wise that allows my message to have the intended impact.

If you are already an excellent communicator, pat yourself on the back! Good job! If you are not quite there, yet, just know it takes time to re-learn the way we speak to others, including our loved ones; but once we have cultivated a culture of good to exceptional communication, we have brought about Environmental well-being, through offering a space of acceptance, and a place where others may thrive and grow. *May these words of my mouth and this meditation of my heart be pleasing in your sight, Lord, my Rock and my Redeemer.*[5]

YOUR WELL WITH GOD JOURNEY

Environmental Wellness can extend into our physical environment through creating orderly, clean, functional, and welcoming spaces. It can even move into the nuances of our environment related to the care we take of our lands, waterways and air. These are all non verbal communications. When we create safe spaces, comfortable and welcoming, clean and responsible, we communicate wellness non-verbally. These things enhance what it means to thrive, and broaden our vision of Environmental Wellness. They do not replace or supplant the meaning applied to Environmental well-being through creating a culture of good communication. Rather, they add to it.

We must begin with harmonious, productive, and accepting relationships with those with whom we occupy space. Meaning, we cannot take care of the physical environment and not give our first love, respect and care to human beings—God's people, even if we disagree with them. In fact, it is here that we move from good to exceptional. It is easy to create an environment of beautiful physical space. It may even be easy to create an environment of acceptance with those with whom we have common interests, but it is those we do not understand or agree with who sharpen our skills to truly reflect the image of God. *But to you who are listening I say: Love your enemies, do good to those who hate you, bless those who curse you, pray for those who mistreat you. If someone slaps you on one cheek, turn to them the other also. If someone takes your coat, do not withhold your shirt from them. Give to everyone who asks you, and if anyone takes what belongs to you, do not demand it back. Do to others as you would have them do to you.*[6]

Take a moment to ask yourself what part of the Environmental Wellness dimension resonated with you most. What are you still thinking about? Jot down a few things to think about later, meditate or pray on, and consider adding images to your vision board that represent your future as a skillful, respectful, and flexible communicator.

ENDNOTES

1. Matthew 7:25, NIV.

2. Ephesians 4:29, NIV.

3. Proverbs 6:11-14, NIV.

4. Proverbs 18:20-21, NIV.

5. Psalm 19:14, NIV.

6. Luke 6:27-31.

OCCUPATIONAL WELLNESS

"When people go to work, they shouldn't have to leave their hearts at home."

–BETTY BENDER

I met Linda in a cocktail lounge. We belong to the same social club in a suburban residential community, and she was seated with a group of millennial women I am acquainted with, who always treat me like one of the girls, even though I am old enough to be the mother of all of them. The usually carefree and animated women seemed today to be having a collectively bad work week, which complemented my state of mind at the time, so I fit right into the conversation. Linda and I introduced ourselves to each other as I pulled-up a seat at the end of the table, and I entered the conversation with ease. The general consensus from the group was lack of verbalized appreciation from direct leadership, yet still receiving full bonuses each year for a job well done.

Being in the health profession, I always found myself working with very nurturing people, where affirmation flowed freely between all staff, regardless of their leadership level. The companies I had worked for were "people-industry" organizations, academic institutions, and public service agencies. I had never worked in corporate America, in a non-people industry. I had often felt fortunate in my work environment and did not feel a shift to a different industry could affect my "wellness equilibrium." I was doing what I had done in my previous job, the work I love, developing engaging health and wellness programs, educating, serving, meeting people right where they are with no judgment. But after 30 years in health and wellness, I found myself for the first time in unfamiliar territory, and now sat at a table with my sisters-in-arms, all expressing similar situations. Then, Linda struck me with a comment, "I would give up 20% of my bonus for a word of appreciation on a regular basis." This is when I began day-dreaming, reminding myself about how intrinsic rewards at work are as important as the paycheck. Just as making good money does not ensure Financial Wellness, having a good job that you are great at and pays well does not always make for Occupational Wellness. It has to be more than a good use of your skills and decent pay. We hear it all the time, it has to be a good fit. But what does that mean? I believe fit is tied to Environmental Wellness. Does the vibe of the work environment fit with my needs, and do I fit with their need? If I need intrinsic rewards such as affirmation, and my environment—i.e. leadership and colleagues—do not offer that, the fit will be off for me, and most likely off for them, as well. Like the snap of a finger, I returned to the present, sitting next to Linda and that is when I heard God's voice; not out loud, but impressed upon me. He said, "You need Linda to review your book." Surprised again by God, I reminded myself that I had not written my book yet. In fact, I was just finishing the proposal which included only Chapter One. How would I know if Linda was even interested in a book rooted in God? So, I disregarded His voice, and spent the next week replaying Linda's words in my head, "I would give up 20% of my bonus for a word of appreciation on a regular basis." I knew I had to address this in the chapter on Occupational Wellness.

You may be familiar with the expression "as fate would have it," but I would like to reintroduce you to that phrase in this way: "As God would have it," Linda and I bumped into each other again a week later, with our husbands. They were joining their dinner group and we were joining ours, yet I migrated to her table, we hugged like old friends, and I sat down beside her. This is when God restated and clarified His previous message to me, "Ask her to read your proposal." At this point, I am certain this is God pressing into my heart, and I am not going to ignore His nudge this time. During my brief conversation with Linda, I managed to mention our church, my faith and this book I was writing. Our initial connection over work woes immediately transformed into a bond over our mutual affection for Jesus.

A couple of weeks later and giving up a Sunday afternoon, Linda came to my home and spent an hour reading my book proposal. The entire time, I sat in the other room with the enemy in my head telling me, "You have no earthly idea what a difficult position you put this woman in." "How is she going to stand in your house and tell you how bad this is." "She's going to have to lie and be gracious to your face." "You are crazy for thinking this book has any value to anyone." Then I would chase the enemy of doubt out of my head and say "just wait and see what she says." Linda feverishly took notes while reading and after about an hour, she emerged with a hug and the most beautiful notes of genuine and specific affirmation to share with me. She loved my book proposal, and wanted to know what comes next! Standing with this new friend in my home, I was instantly experiencing Occupational Wellness. I was doing my "job" and I felt valued, and I was not getting paid. I was not at my traditional day job. I was writing a book that had not been on my "to do" list...ever. Before sending my proposal to the literary agent, Linda was the only person I let read it. I barely knew her, but I knew I could trust her to be honest, *and responsible,* with her thoughts and feelings. I knew God had made the connection for us.

OCCUPATIONAL DESTINY

Occupational Wellness helps us take an intimate look at what is our personal "calling" in life. To accomplish this, we need to examine what we are doing for employment or lack of employment, what we *want* to do, and determine how we can achieve our inner desires in our current occupation, amplify our work situation, make slight adjustments in our occupation, or even take a profound about-face! I love Occupational Wellness because it is tied to seeking and discovering our anointed destiny in life! For many, this involves working for others, for some it involves working for ourselves, and there are also those for which it involves working in the home for no external pay. Yet through all the self-searching to find our work destiny, we have to stay mindful of the truth that God will lead us to it. We must remember that He has not only planted our occupational desires in our destiny DNA, He has gifted us with a skill-set and talent that makes it positively our calling.

Our destiny DNA, strengths, and talent may all point to a career in one particular occupation in *our* mind, but God can fulfill our desires in an entirely different line of work than we may have imagined. He does this through offering us opportunity. Many people pass on the opportunity to step into their destiny because they do not recognize it as their destiny. They have in mind what they want to do and miss what they are *meant* to do. For example, my ego had been thinking for about three years that the next step for my occupational title of Senior Program Manager, was to advance to the title Director, Vice President, and eventually Chief Wellness Officer; but God wanted to advance me to the title Author. This can be scary in mortal life, because *Author* does not have any salary expectation attached to it. When we think of occupations, salary is typically a driving force. I had to open my mind, reframe my thoughts, and reaffirm my faith. *Unless the Lord builds the house, the builders labor in vain.*[1]

We spend so much of our life in our employment and God does not intend our work to be drudgery. As I said in Chapter One, He has set-up each of us with undeniable gifts and a divine set of skills that, when we uncover our gifts and put them to work, we will feel fulfilled, and we will be working in service to Him. Everyone serves. If we are currently in a job where we are not satisfied, we may need to find our service right where we are, while

> I HAD TO OPEN MY MIND, REFRAME MY THOUGHTS, AND REAFFIRM MY FAITH.

we look and wait for opportunities to achieve our calling. We must be excellent with the opportunity God has in front of us right now, in order to prepare ourselves for the opportunity He has in our future. I believe it will come through prayer, watching, listening, taking action, and letting His will be done. *Many are the plans in a person's heart, but it is the Lord's purpose that prevails.*[2]

We will know we are operating in our divine work destination because we will feel fulfilled, enriched, and satisfied with what we are doing. We will also know because it will serve others, even though it may not be a job in the service industry. It will serve because our work destiny is to serve. It is my firm belief that work satisfaction is the outcome we receive when we let our work become service. Important to the concept of finding our work destiny is knowing that destiny is often, if not usually, a moving target. We can enjoy Occupational Wellness in one job, be promoted, move or get laid off, and find it again in another job. This is how we grow and add to our ability to contribute.

IT'S NOT ABOUT THE JOB, IT'S ABOUT THE FIT

I want to return to the discussion about the importance of the environment in our Occupational Wellness. I associated *fit* with Environmental Wellness, but all parties cannot necessarily determine fit in a single job interview or a series of interviews. Fit is not truly able to be assessed until everyone is established in their respective roles and working together in the workplace. Sure, there are psycho-social assessments and tests that work to avoid a bad fit, but they are not always going to be successful. The primary reason is the power imbalance during the hiring process. The employee wants or needs a job and the employer has the power to give the job. Despite the fact that we are in a time where prospective employees are learning to know their value, and are urged to use it to be selective about who they will work for, the reality is that they are looking for a job, they have bills to pay, jobs are competitive, and the hiring decision is not theirs. Employees take a job with no useful information about the teammates they will work with, while employers know the prospective employee's work history, have completed reference checks, and usually have the results of a psycho-social assessment.

I once took and passed a series of psycho-social assessments for a position that landed me in the middle of a work environment that was not a good fit me. What I really needed to know in advance of taking the job, were some of the decisions that were made regarding my reporting structure. Apparently, not everyone on the team was on board with the structure. I was set-up. Not on purpose, but believe me, it was a set-up. Fortunately, we all worked through the situation, but it took a year and a lot of anguish on my part, to get there. God was present in that growing process for all of us. For me, because I prayed for His guidance and for them, because I prayed for them whether or not they prayed on their own. *After Job had prayed for his friends, the LORD restored his fortunes and gave him twice as much as he had before.*[3]

While employers are doing a good job trying to assess fit prior to extending offers of employment, it is important to note that employers who are part of a problem in the workplace do not typically realize they are the core of a brewing problem, or they are in denial. I re-emphasize, Occupational Wellness is dependent on having a work environment that is conducive to thriving for all. Shae is educated as a scientist and an engineer, but after a short stint in her industry, she moved to a new city, and landed a job in a construction-related company doing inside sales. She liked the job well enough because her supervisor treated her with respect and consideration. The trouble was, she had no opportunity for advancement and she has a lot of ambition and talent. As she weighed her options, she decided after two years she needed to make a move, and went hard after a job in outside sales for a different construction-related company, and landed the job. There, she encountered a highly toxic and dysfunctional work environment. I am not talking about one person who is toxic and the rest are great, so she could overlook the one. I am talking about toxic and dysfunctional, meaning there was one overwhelmingly toxic leader that influenced the rest of the workforce to be dysfunctional—insecure, uncertain and "walk on eggshells" in most interactions in the office.

The first time Shae heard the boss refer to an employee as "retarded," she knew she was in trouble. Shae is a highly gifted woman, very open-minded and empathetic toward others. In addition to being well-educated, she is a skilled communicator and a trained domestic mediator. Her interpersonal skill level is exceptional. She put those qualities to work in this environment with the hope of perpetuating culture change, but mostly to achieve some personal work satisfaction. The beginning of the end occurred when Shae had been berated by her boss for three days over leaving photos out of a proposal. She took her lumps, accepted responsibility both verbally and in writing, but on the third day her boss, having already previously referred to her as ignorant and retarded (in a 21st century work world), was now fabricating his own reality in some masochistic exercise to continue the conflict until she reached some predetermined breaking point in his mind. Was he intentionally trying to make her cry or fall apart? She was teetering on the brink of both, but yielded to neither.

Shae looked him in the eye and told him, "I can't do this. I can't work here for you." She gathered her things and left. The worst part of this is that she was already so beaten down after four months of watching and experiencing verbal abuse, that she did not feel relief; rather, she felt failure. She was concerned about having no income to contribute to her household, and felt like a failure having two college degrees and no career. That is how quickly a highly skilled person, with plenty of "wins" under her belt, can be brought down by the enemy. Yet, God has the final say in all things. In less than 24 hours, God opened a door, and in faith and a testament to resiliency, Shae had the keen eye to step through. Shae had still been in touch with her previous employer. They had not had success in hiring the right person to fill her previously vacated position, so she contacted them, and asked if they would be willing to have her come back. They enthusiastically welcomed her back; and although her compensation was not as high as her salary was in the toxic job, the environment provided what she needed to get up each day and go to the office to put in an honest day's work. Shae has not found her divine calling in life, but she has Occupational Wellness and has higher levels of well-being in some of the other dimensions to help boost those where she still has work to do.

It is important to address the Occupational Wellness of those who work in the home as homemakers and family caretakers—basically an uncompensated occupation. Occupational Wellness is very much part of their wellness model. In fact, I believe stay-at-home people who are satisfied and fulfilled in their role make the case for the importance and value of intrinsic rewards. They do not draw a paycheck, yet they are satisfied and enjoy Occupational Wellness. One of my favorite friends, Carol, could have been classified as a stay-at-home mom when her children were growing up, and could now be classified as a stay-at-home wife. Yet, even after earning a college degree, she chose this occupation just as I chose my career. And Carol excelled (excels) at her work! Not to diminish the role of her husband and of her children, when they were living in the home, but Carol all-but single-handedly tends the pastures, fences, and livestock of their farm. She is a natural nurturer of living creatures, human and otherwise. Carol definitely followed her inner voice to her anointed profession, and enjoys Occupational Wellness. Not everyone is put-together to do the job Carol does with the same level of passion and excellence. I dare say I am not. That is the beauty of following our dreams; they are unique to each of us. Carol has shared with me in the past that she is agnostic. She does not have a strong religious or traditional spiritual practice. In this way we are opposites, yet we are very similar and enjoy each other very much. This is because of God. Whether Carol knows God the way I know God, I am 100% certain that God knows Carol and does a very good work through her every day! Her "fit" for the job He has led her to, is clearly an anointed one.

SELF-EFFICACY AND SETTING GOALS

I want to introduce the term self-efficacy, if you are not already familiar with it. There is no other word like it and no good synonym, at least none that I have found. I love the word self-efficacy. Self-efficacy refers to an individual's belief in his or her capacity to execute behaviors necessary to produce specific performance attainments (Bandura, 1977, 1986, 1997). My lay person definition is that self-efficacy is our belief and confidence in our capability to accomplish basically anything. This is not to be confused with our self-confidence or feelings of self-worth, which focus on the confidence we feel in ourselves as human beings. Self-efficacy is instead focused on our confidence in our ability to "do" something, anything. It ties in well with the concept of Locus of Control that we discussed in Chapter Four, and research suggests that those who have a high level of self-efficacy are more likely to become successful at the things they attempt to do. In my younger years, I thought I got to self-efficacy through sheer grit and determination. As I have matured in my relationship with God, I have come to realize my high level of self-efficacy is solidly founded in my belief that *I can do all this through Him who gives me strength* (Philippians, 4:13 NIV). I rarely look at a situation and think, "I can't because...." If I do, I use the concept of Cognitive Restructuring to re-frame that, and I turn to scripture to support my words with belief and faith.

If we are to achieve Occupational Wellness, or any dimension of wellness for that matter, we must strengthen our feeling of self-efficacy.

If we want to achieve a certain knowledge to obtain a certain job, or position ourselves to attain a specific career, then we must know we can do it. God gave us the *knowing*. We simply must tap into the *knowing*, put our faith in Him, and move from head to heart in believing. We have to set goals. We cannot achieve a goal if we do not set one. This is why I emphasize the use of vision boards and ask you after each chapter to write down one or more take-aways that resonate with you. This is essential to achieving a goal. If you can see it, it is easier to achieve it. You must see it with your physical eye, then you must see it with your mind's eye, then you must feel it in your heart, then you can realize it. *Write down the revelation and make it plain on tablets so that a herald may run with it. For the revelation awaits an appointed time; it speaks of the end, and will not prove false. Though it linger, wait for it; it will certainly come and will not delay.*[4]

Here, I would like to offer a deeper look at setting occupational goals. We have to dissect each goal and find the honesty in our goal. This can help us find a better path to success, and also help us separate our God-given heart's desires from the enemy's desire to satisfy our ego and derail our achievement of our anointed calling. In my story in Chapter One about having a goal to be a broadcast journalist, that was a good goal, set when I was 18 years old; but had I dissected the goal, I would have been more honest if I said, I wanted to be *heard*. I used to do the morning announcements over the intercom at my high school. I did not ask to do this, it was asked of me. Most likely because I had an effervescent personality, I liked to talk and had no trouble in drama club so, certainly, I could follow a script. This is likely where the broadcast journalism seed grew. Had I looked more closely at my truer goal which was to be *heard*, I could follow up by asking myself, *what do I want people to hear me say?*

I do not know what the answer would have been at age 18, because it did not occur to me to ask myself that, but I can answer that now. I do indeed want to be heard. I want the words I say to inspire people.

What do I want to inspire them to do? I want to inspire people to believe that God has made them perfectly and wonderfully, and they are beautiful inside and out, and He has not left any of us out of this promise. I want to inspire listeners to fall in love with God in themselves, not in a conceited way, but in a spiritual way, where they can achieve self-efficacy, knowing they can become more than they could even conceive. I want to inspire listeners to believe they can feel joy every day, and at those times when they do not feel joy, they know it is just a fleeting moment, and that joy will return. I do not just want to be *heard* offering inspiration and truths about God, I want to be heard telling how we achieve this self-efficacy. Some of us can be told nurturing things and blaze our own trail, and others of us need to hear the nurturing words and be given a starting place. These chapters represent the starting place, or the suggestion that the starting place may not be where you think.

I COULD FOLLOW UP BY ASKING MYSELF, *WHAT DO I WANT PEOPLE TO HEAR ME SAY?*

With Occupational Wellness, the starting place is with setting a goal, then dissecting it. Even if you think you know your goal, even if you feel like you are living your goal, please take a moment to meditate on your heart's desire. Sit still with God, right now. Focus on your breath for five minutes and just listen and feel God. Ask Him, what does He want you to do in order to serve Him? Then sit and listen. Then come back to the next paragraph.

What did He say? If you didn't feel Him impress anything onto your heart, that is okay. Use what is in your head. Either way, write down your occupational goal. Maybe it is in your current job or another career. Do not limit your goal because God has no limits. Now, do what I did, with my broadcast journalism example; Dissect your goal. What is it about that career that draws you to it? What skills do you have that lead you there? What feelings do you have? Are your feelings self-serving, like fame and money or are your feelings altruistic, serving others, or somewhere in between. Do not chastise yourself if the feelings or desires seem selfish or conceited. Rather, explore your truth in those thoughts and feelings. For example, wanting to be famous may not be about fame as much as it is about wanting to feel relevant, or respected, or smart, or beautiful.

You cannot find your calling until you peel away the layers to reveal your true self that God created for a purpose. He cares *not* about your brains or beauty, He cares about how you can use the brains, beauty, or other talents He gave you to glorify *Him*. How do we glorify God with our brains or our compassion or our intuitiveness? By inventing ways to care for others, caring for our earth, protecting freedom, advocating for others, keeping a worksite clean and safe for others, teaching someone to read or write, etc. How do we glorify God with our beauty? If people are drawn to our beauty, we make sure that beautiful things come out of our mouth to share with them, and beautiful gestures and behaviors are expressed through our generosity toward them. This is how we develop and experience occupational well-being.

HELPING CO-WORKERS

There is also great value in helping others achieve their Occupational Wellness. In our discussion about the importance of intrinsic rewards in our work, we need to strive to be that co-worker or leader who fosters gratitude in the workplace. We need to make sure we are not following the lead of others to ostracize a co-worker or leave them out. We need to always be inclusive, regardless of how awkward we feel with others or certain personalities. Nobody should ever be left out of the team. We need to be in tune with our co-workers and have at least a minimal understanding of their personal life, so we can be supportive of them. Most of us spend the majority of our day at work, and we need to love the people with whom we work. Love them, you ask? Yes, love them! You do not have to like how they behave and you do not have to spend time with them outside of work, but you must love them as human beings and treat them with respect, even when they do not treat you with respect, even if you are looking for your next job and a way out. You honor yourself and God when you do so, and you can leave without regret if you leave. At minimum, you can leave every day to go home, and know you did your part, and the rest is in God's hands. At maximum, you model goodness and respect, and others will experience it, feel it, and hopefully start to tap into their own goodness and respect as they reflect your Godliness.

We must also do our part to recognize the gifts of others in the work place, and be willing to give them a hand-up to promotion, when appropriate. In doing this, we promote their feelings of Occupational Wellness. We do not live our best self when we fear that someone will outshine us, so we keep them in a position where they cannot grow. They will likely end up leaving and taking their talent with them, anyway. We also need to nurture low achievers so they can realize their strengths; and if we are in a position of leadership, and a low or marginal achiever is not making the progress they need, we can do them a service of cutting them loose, so they may move on toward their anointed destination. This is an awkward situation for most of us, to let a person go. I am not sure there is a right way to spare them the feelings of loss and rejection, but there are ways to diminish their negative feelings. This starts with preparing a "what's next" plan for them. Even when firing someone for egregious behavior, they are human beings with feelings, and we want to help mitigate any feelings of despair. We can do this by writing them a list of our perception of their strengths, offering them connections to their way forward, and being warm and respectful. When a person is fired, or even laid off, they may feel in a fog over the event and need a way through. Be that way through—don't just cut them off. Human Resources, Risk Management, and Legal professionals may disagree and have concern over liability, but I am a believer that we need to keep the *human*, or maybe the *humane*, in Human Resources, and treat our exiting co-workers the way we would like to be treated under similar circumstances. Each time I read or hear a news story of another horrific workplace violence incident, I have wondered if we restructure protocols around firing or laying off employees, might we be able to stave off the desperate or diabolical nature of those who have the propensity for workplace violence. It is hard to know, and we cannot be held responsible for the unpredictable behavior of a troubled individual. I just wonder if we can avoid fully disenfranchising the employee as part of the legal process of letting them go, and find a way to show compassion and care, rather than operating from an abundance of caution for fear of a potential lawsuit.

YOUR WELL WITH GOD JOURNEY

Returning to the goal setting exercise we completed earlier, take a moment and ask yourself if anything else from this chapter about Occupational Wellness has resonated with you. What are you still thinking about? Jot down a few things to think about later, meditate or pray on, and consider adding to your vision board.

ENDNOTES

1. Psalm 127:1, NIV.
2. Proverbs 19:21, NIV.
3. Job 42:10, NIV.
4. Habakkuk 2:2-3, NIV.

Chapter 7

INTELLECTUAL
WELLNESS

"Creativity is intelligence having fun."
–ALBERT EINSTEIN

A s I shared previously, I used to have trouble distinguishing the difference between Intellectual Wellness and Occupational Wellness. The word "creative" helped me get past that. A quick search of the internet or a thesaurus will yield these words as synonymous with the word *intellectual*: Mental, cerebral, cognitive, rational, psychological, abstract, conceptual, theoretical, analytical, logical and academic. In the past, I have often associated the concept of intellectualism with a level of "high-brow" book knowledge, but the inclusion of the word *abstract* in the list above helps me make sense of why Intellectual Wellness extends to those who are creative, in addition to those who are theoretical and analytical. According to the Substance Abuse and Mental Health Services Administration, Intellectual Wellness is found in our ability to recognize our creative abilities and find ways to expand our knowledge and skills.

Given this definition, Intellectual Wellness can, indeed, be closely tied to Occupational Wellness when a person continually expands their knowledge to grow and create new and better ways to be effective in their employment. But mostly, intellectual well-being is associated with staying creatively and intellectually stimulated, regardless of whether or not it supports our occupation. Think of it as our "extra-curricular" activities.

DISCOVERING INTELLECTUAL WELLNESS

How do we discover what our intellectual calling is? Do we discover *it* or does *it* discover *us*? Intellectual Wellness is prompted by our curiosity. Therefore, it can be one of the easiest dimensions in which to achieve wellness. When we are intellectually stimulated and we feed our creative and intellectual mind, our self-esteem naturally elevates. Elevated self-esteem increases our emotional well-being, and it also increases our confidence in developing social connections with people of similar interests, thus improving our Mental and Social Wellness – another example of how success in one dimension serves as a catalyst to success in others.

In the last chapter, I told the story of Shae and her continuing journey to find a higher level of Occupational Wellness. I also mentioned that while she works on her career and waits on the Lord to help her find the right door, Shae has strengthened other dimensions of her WELL WITH GOD model. Intellectual Wellness is one of Shae's strengths. Shae may create bids for commercial construction projects by day, but by night and on the weekends, she is a superhero! Literally! Although Shae has never been a major video gamer, voracious comic book reader or movie addict, she had enough exposure to all three to become enthralled with the super human elements and fantasy of super hero characters and the out-of-this world design aesthetics of the costumes and supernatural elements of these characters. This led Shae to begin creating costumes and appearing at Comic Conventions (ComiCon) throughout her state and other national venues. This interest further spurred Shae to become a pattern-maker, seamstress, a constructor of (foam) armor, and a leather-smith. She has even incorporated lighting and hydraulics into some of her creations. Her costumes are so intricately handmade, expertly crafted and well-designed that she has won several small competitions and has been invited to appear as a guest at events. Shae sometimes runs a live video stream while she works, answers questions and generally has fun doing it. She has definitely "recognized her creative abilities and expanded her knowledge and skills" to become good at her craft. *And he has filled him with the Spirit of God, with wisdom, with understanding, with knowledge and with all kinds of skills.*[1]

But there is more interconnectedness that Intellectual Wellness has unlocked for Shae, and illustrates how all of us can follow God's lead to unexpected divine destinations. Shae describes that she never liked to be called on in class because she felt self-conscious. Now, Shae is interviewed about her costume-making on camera, and is charming and engaging. She chats easily during weekly live-stream events and greets the public at conventions and appearances without reservation. What happened? It was not simple maturity that happened for Shae. She had to connect with the person God designed her to be. She had to be in her element, which gets back to the issue of *fit* that we talked about previously. Shae has found her fit or tribe in the cosplay industry. There was a time she tried to find her tribe in pageant competition during high school, in sorority life at college, and in other social circles as a young woman. She found it frustrating and sometimes felt defective as a human and as a friend.

Technically, this is Social Wellness territory which we will discuss more in Chapter Eight, but in this case Social Wellness became a by-product of Shae achieving intellectual well-being. She found her social tribe through developing her Intellectual Wellness, without any effort at all. Shae may not yet have the full complement of Occupational Wellness that she desires, but she got a *buy-one, get-one* offer when she followed her God-given gift of intricacy into costume-making. It landed Shae in her own world of creative design and construction, satisfying her Intellectual Wellness needs, and carried her right into friendships and relationships, leading to a diverse and supportive Social Wellness network. I want to reiterate the description I gave above, "she followed her God-given gift of *intricacy* into costume-making." This is an excellent example of dissecting a goal as we explore our destiny. The emphasis is not on the goal of costume-making; the emphasis is on the gifting from God of "intricacy," which led to costume making. *And so you will inherit a double portion in your land, and everlasting joy will be yours.*[2]

Intellectual Wellness is often found in a person's hobbies, but I worry about using the term hobby. Hobbies are often associated with being a pastime, a diversion, or even a fad. This sounds diminishing to me. Rather than diminish the word *hobby,* I propose we elevate it to its rightful position of Intellectual Wellness, where it joins all the other cerebral, abstract and creative areas of fulfillment. For many, having their intellectual outlet is the primary aspect of their life that supports their mental well-being, especially in the face of yet-unfulfilled other dimensions of wellness. Whether a person builds model airplanes, handcrafts furniture, participates in gladiator events, is a voracious scientific reader, knits baby blankets, or enjoys crossword puzzles, the mental and physical stimulation and satisfaction they get from these activities is very important to their well-being.

One of my favorite things about Intellectual Wellness is its ability to break the barrier of judgment about a person. Intellectual Wellness often reveals the most fascinating things about people that have nothing to do with the way we know that person at work, church, or in the community. We may know a person at work for their accounting prowess or a person behind a counter at our favorite coffee shop for their great customer service. Then we learn that they have this entirely different "alter ego" such as the one I described with Shae in the beginning of this chapter. I worked for a company that had a chaplain service that provided onsite chaplains to circulate, visit and generally be available to employees during the workday and after hours, if they were in need. It was a service I previously was unaware even existed, but it was invaluable and truly demonstrated the company's commitment to the holistic well-being of its workforce. I helped coordinate this service as part of my job, so I had the occasion to get to know the chaplains, aside from their work as spiritual counselors. One of the chaplains was a painter and had illustrated a children's book. I found that fascinating about her, and I got to see her talent when she showed me the book she illustrated. From that point, I did not see her as a pastor. I saw her as a pastor, an artist, and because of our continued conversations, as a receptionist at a used car dealership, and as a fashionista. Look how multi-dimensional she is! I know her spiritual, intellectual and occupational well-being without ever having a formal discussion about the dimensions of wellness. I hope these connections are helping you expand your own perspective of who you are and how multi-dimensional you are as a human being, and the mosaic you represent, unparalleled by any other. You are, indeed, a perfect masterpiece of God.

> WHEN WE ALLOW OURSELVES TO SEE THE MULTI-DIMENSIONAL ASPECTS OF A PERSON, WE REMOVE ACCIDENTAL BARRIERS WE HAVE PLACED AROUND A PERSON'S IDENTITY

For those of us who are not always comfortable starting conversations with others, especially others we do not know well, I encourage you to practice starting conversations with people by asking about their interests outside of their professional life. "What's your favorite thing to do on your day off?" is a great start. Even if we are not judgmental by nature, through having these conversations with people, we remove accidental barriers we have placed around a person's identity in our mind. In so doing, we expand our Spiritual Wellness, because any time we open our hearts more to the people we encounter throughout a given day, we open our hearts to God in them and God in us. It is a beautiful thing. *Dear friends, let us love one another, for love comes from God. Everyone who loves has been born of God and knows God.*[3]

YOUR WELL WITH GOD JOURNEY

It is not uncommon for us to have interests outside of our family and work life but feel like we do not have time to pursue them. Those creative and intellectual interests, urges, and passions are part of our destiny, planted by God. They are part of the map for our life. They enrich us and bring out new elements of our personality and talents in our skill bank. They offer enhanced opportunities for us to serve in ways we may not have imagined. When we leave them "untapped," we short-change ourselves, and we short-change those who would be blessed and inspired by us. Take a moment to sit still with God and reflect on your Intellectual Wellness. If you are actively engaged in your Intellectual Wellness interest, consider how it has positively influenced your life and the life of others. Plan how you can maintain, continue to balance, or possibly grow your intellectual well-being. If you have not developed or fully developed your Intellectual Wellness, use your stillness and reflection to consider what is left in your gift box from God that you have not unwrapped or unpacked? Listen. Receive. Develop a plan forward. Start with writing it down for your goals list or vision board. *Every good and perfect gift is from above, coming down from the Father of the heavenly lights, who does not change like shifting shadows.*[4]

ENDNOTES

1. Exodus 30:31, NIV.

2. Isaiah 61:7, NIV.

3. 1 John 4:7, NIV.

4. James 1:17, NIV.

SOCIAL WELLNESS

"You can't achieve anything entirely by yourself.
There's a support system that is a basic requirement
of human existence. To be happy and successful on
earth, you just have to have people that you rely on."

–MICHAEL SCHUR

Social Wellness is tribal. I said this when I first introduced the concept. I love the word *tribe*. It sounds primitive, but it never goes out of style. We all need our tribe, our place we belong, where understanding and support is exchanged effortlessly and genuinely between tribe members. Social Wellness involves developing a sense of connectedness and belonging with individuals or groups of individuals who "get" us and who are nurturing, empathetic, affirming, and able to challenge us, yet not be unkind. These are some of the essential ingredients of a well-developed social support system, and the outcome is social well-being. These connections help us understand and experience the value of authentic, healthy relationships. This is our tribe. These are our peeps, our familia, our cheerleaders, our crew. These become the first places we get the opportunity to serve others. *Greater love has no one than this: to lay down one's life for one's friends.*[1]

During Open House at our daughter's elementary school one year, the principal urged parents not to come to the school to have lunch in the cafeteria with our children. I was a helicopter mom and did not particularly like hearing this, but I really liked the explanation the principal gave, so I complied without resistance. She explained that our children have very structured schedules, but the lunch and recess time is the unstructured time that allows children to develop and practice social skills. So true! From the earliest of ages when we are developing our first social skills, to the aged years when we have well-developed social networks and may be losing friends to illness and natural causes, we experience the impact of Social Wellness. This dimension of wellness helps us learn how to interact with others, how to share and resolve conflict, and how to show compassion and empathy. It also creates opportunities for us to gain insights into different cultures, spiritual practices, and family structures, and embrace them.

Developing meaningful relationships can be difficult for some people. For some of us, it happens naturally—we are extroverts, never met a stranger, or have a natural affinity for Social Wellness. For others, this may not be the case. My recurring theme is that many of us find our way to one dimension of wellness through another, so if we are lacking in our social well-being, despite efforts to develop close relationships, our path may not be the straight and narrow; rather, it may be a winding road through one or more of the other dimensions. Wellness is not just a journey, it is an adventure!

VOLUNTEERISM

We develop our social support network through family, work, places of worship, neighborhoods, formal organizations, online and also by chance encounters. One of the widest reaching opportunities for developing social networks is through volunteerism. Unless we are volunteering as part of our workplace culture or our child's educational system, or are court-ordered to volunteer as part of our penance for a legal infraction, volunteering is typically motivated by our passion. Remember, our passions are planted deep inside us by God as part of our personality DNA. Volunteerism is service, and is performed for intrinsic benefits rather than compensation. Yet, it offers great rewards— rewards that feed other dimensions of wellness, such as

VOLUNTEERISM IS SERVICE, AND IS PERFORMED FOR INTRINSIC BENEFITS RATHER THAN COMPENSATION intellectual, occupational, mental, and spiritual well-being. Whether we are serving on a Board of Directors, tutoring algebra, sewing costumes for a play, raising money for a building, or handing out groceries at the local food pantry, we are promoting our Social Wellness through our volunteerism.

You may wonder why volunteerism is not categorized as Intellectual or Occupational Wellness. Actually, it can easily fit into either of those dimensions as well, and if you are more comfortable viewing it from the perspective of one of the other dimensions, there are no hard and fast rules, because wellness is so finely woven together. The reason I place volunteerism in the social dimension is primarily because of those who receive our service. Our focus is not necessarily on the fulfillment we experience over putting our God-gifted skills and talents to work; the focus is on our social and spiritual connection with the people or cause we serve.

When we are serving, we enter into a social relationship with the recipient(s) of that service. For many of the recipients, we become part of their social support system, whether short term or long term, and whether we feel the same close relationship with them as they seem to feel toward us. Because we enter into volunteerism out of a desire to serve, we typically experience reciprocity in our feelings toward them. But have you ever had an acquaintance or friend who considered your friendship more integral to their life than you realized, or even stronger than your own feelings toward them? That may be a hard thing to admit or accept, but we do experience this at times. When we experience this, we may not want to force a chemistry that we do not naturally feel; but it is important to respect and value the honor a person has placed on you, deserved or not. Just as God expects us to be good stewards of our finances, he expects us to be good stewards of the relationships he has placed in our path. *Each of you should use whatever gift you have received to serve others, as faithful stewards of God's grace in its various forms.*[2]

THE ACADEMICS OF SOCIAL WELLNESS

Adding to the Social Wellness conversation, I would like us to consider an academic aspect of developing social support systems. To accomplish this, I need to talk about strokes and theory. A stroke is a unit of recognition. Any kind of recognition, verbal or nonverbal. Strokes can be positive or negative. For example, a positive stroke would be smiling, waving or saying hello when someone greets you. Alternatively, a negative stroke may be ignoring someone when they greet you, despite clearly knowing they are making an effort to acknowledge you. Positive and negative strokes are present in physical affection, as well as physical violence; therefore, it is an easy conclusion that the type of strokes we receive are critical in the Social Wellness we experience in our lives. Whether we are cognizant of it or not, strokes are essential to our perception of what we have to offer others and, importantly, they are instrumental to what we allow others to offer us.

A theory I learned in the early part of my career that made a lot of sense to me is the Stroke Bank Theory. I learned about the Stroke Bank Theory from the book *Self-Esteem: A Family Affair* by Jean Illsley Clarke. Essentially, it suggests that our ability to be present in a relationship, to give and receive strokes depends on the level of our "Stroke Bank." The Stroke Bank is described like a bank vault of money, except the collateral is not dollars—it is strokes. When we have a high stroke bank level, we can easily give positive strokes away to others. Further, we actually attract strokes that keep our stroke level high, because giving out positivity returns it back to us, like interest in a bank. At the other end of the spectrum, we have individuals who have such low stroke bank levels and are so disenfranchised that they often cannot accept and receive positive strokes that come to them. Many of the people in this category suffer from illness, are hospitalized, incarcerated, or otherwise institutionalized. In Chapter Four, when I talked about being inpatient in the psychiatric unit of a hospital, I was in a state of the lowest stroke bank level in this illustration. Today, I enjoy the highest level in the stroke bank. There are also a couple of levels in between where a person is just getting by, not able to give or receive strokes; or are toward the top of the stroke bank, so they are able to offer and receive some positive strokes, but they are not necessarily attracting them abundantly. Our stroke level can shift throughout life and life events. You may imagine from our other discussions that we have a lot to do with this.

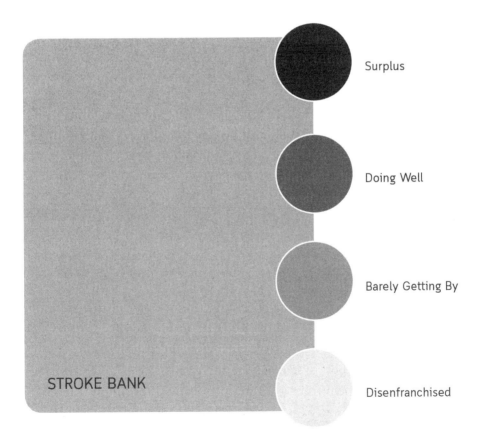

The purpose of my introduction of the Stroke Bank Theory is my application of it to Social Wellness. It makes sense to me that when a person is at or towards the top of the stroke bank, they are more likely to be able to participate in gratifying social relationships. They can both give and receive in the relationship building process. When a relationship develops fully, if one of the parties drops lower in their stroke bank, the other party is now attuned to their family member or friend, and is willing to offer support to build up their loved one. We have sometimes thought about relationships in terms of percentages when it comes to giving and receiving, meaning that it should be a 50-50 relationship. This is realistic in theory, but in practice, healthy support systems do not keep a metric regarding who gives or receives more in the relationship. I am not referring to abusive relationships. I am referring to relationships with the potential to develop into wholesomeness without compromising the safety and security of either party.

If we are to be responsive to each other, we have to be willing to be servant-minded, meaning there will be times, for long or short periods, when we give 80% and the other person is perceived to be giving 20%. But what if their 20% is 100% of what they have to offer? What if they are in the disenfranchised category due to illness or abuse, and they do not have the current state of resiliency that allows them to give at the other party's level; yet they are still giving 100% of what they have to offer? Consider further my earlier example of having a friend who thinks more of a relationship than the other party, regardless of their respective stroke bank levels. From their perspective, they assign greater value to the interactions they have shared. Their frame of reference is different. These two examples make a convincing point that relationships in healthy, social support systems come in various shapes and sizes, and we must receive them from a servant perspective, not simply a receiver perspective, if we are to experience social well-being and connectedness.

For those with low or disenfranchised stroke levels, they are not willing and able to engage in healthy relationships, because they are in a place where they feel and believe they have nothing to give emotionally. They can easily give in to abusive and toxic relationships when at this level, fulfilling the role of both the giver of the negativity and the receiver of it. At the lowest of lows, this results in jail, prison, sickness and hospitalization. At this point, they are essentially "emotionally unavailable." The term *emotionally unavailable* may be used for other types of personality or behavior quirks, but I believe it profoundly applies here. If we have ever met someone whom we thought was unfriendly or generally unresponsive to our effort to be friendly, it is possible they may have been receptive at a different time in their life, but this particular time is one from which they feel unable to reciprocate positivity.

Aside from abusive situations, which we must avoid for our safety and social well-being; If we take it a step further and persevere with the "lukewarm" individual, even though they are unresponsive, we may actually be a catalyst for helping raise their stroke level, and a wonderful relationship may develop. At minimum, we help lift up another person, and we do not have to entrench ourselves in their lives in the process, if it does not feel right. Oftentimes, however, we do not get that far, because we experience their negativity, make a judgment that this person does not like us, and we move on. *Therefore, as God's chosen people, holy and dearly loved, clothe yourselves with compassion, kindness, humility, gentleness and patience. Bear with each other and forgive one another if any of you has a grievance against someone. Forgive as the Lord forgave you.*[3]

We can also be judgmental of ourselves, especially if we see ourselves in the lower half of the stroke bank. Armed with the Stroke Bank Theory, we must be ever-mindful to work with God to get ourselves out of dire straits. While God can deliver us from anything, He does want us to actively participate with Him in our growth and development. Then, we must do maintenance to keep our stroke level above the midway point and move it into the surplus area, where we are giving and receiving positive strokes freely and frequently.

This begs the question, "How do we do maintenance to keep our stroke level high?" We seek out and surround ourselves with nurturing, empathetic, challenging, yet kind individuals. We also look for opportunities to lift up someone else with our loving kindness. This is where we experience high social well-being. If we are naturally judgmental or suspicious of others until we get to know them, we are operating in the mid to lower level of the stroke bank, and we will certainly attract the same type of personalities into our relationships. We open the door to what we get by how we give.

WE OPEN THE DOOR TO WHAT WE GET BY HOW WE GIVE

Our individual stroke bank can change at any time depending on how we respond to events in our lives. This ties stroke level to resiliency, and to our previous Mental Wellness discussion on Cognitive Restructuring. While we can expect our stroke bank to fluctuate or dip, tending to our frame of mind is every bit as important as tending to our diet or bank account. We must exchange toxic thinking for positive thinking, and toxic social connections and activities with positive ones.

Many of our challenges in developing relationships with people who cross our path are not necessarily tied to one of us having a low stroke bank level. They may be simple misinterpretations, misunderstandings, and judgments. My best friend to this day is someone I met in high school and we did not have immediate chemistry. Gwendolyn was on the varsity cheer squad and I was a new member of the junior varsity squad. We were assigned lockers next to each other in a special section for the campus athletes. Gwendolyn rarely responded when I greeted her with my over abundant personality. I tried chatting her up, smiling, making small talk. She was having none of it. At first, I was tempted to think she was stuck-up but God laid it on my heart that she was not stuck-up, she was shy. How can a varsity cheerleader be shy? Gwendolyn was shy in person, but not shy when cheering! I adjusted my expectation that she meet me at my energy level and I met her at hers. We became best friends, but only because I resisted my temptation to judge and dismiss her. *Do not judge, or you too will be judged. For in the same way you judge others, you will be judged, and with the measure you use, it will be measured to you.*[4]

SOCIAL MEDIA WELLNESS

Social media can either be an outstanding extension of our social well-being, or the bane of our existence. Notice I said extension. Social media has no ability to supplant face-to-face contact as a support system. Spirits need to connect and chemistry needs to be experienced firsthand. This is the stuff of God. Without the human contact in your social support system, your essence of God is missing. You can craft your social media posts and content messages with love, and that is important, but it will never be able to replace *you*. It can, however, supplement, and it can be a great supplement!

The opposite becomes true for social media gone wrong. The one-on-one encounters with bullies are painful and can leave scars, but they do not perpetuate themselves in the face-to-face medium like social media does. When it is over, it is over, and we can hopefully avoid another in-person encounter with the bully. Online bullying, however, lives forever, and can extend to unfathomable reaches. Social media gives bullies an opportunity to aggressively and relentlessly pursue victims. Social media also facilitates the creation of bullies. How so? Social media is a temptress. People who struggle with judgment and ego toward others, but are normally not confrontational, can develop simulated courage under the influence of anonymity or virtual reality. The rule on social media is simple: use it sparingly, and do not follow it to our detriment.

That may be easier said than done, but it is truly this simple. We must use social media sparingly as a Social Wellness tool, and choose to enrich our lives with the authenticity of in-person, connected relationships.

DEMONSTRATING RESPECT

The communication skills from Chapter Five, Environmental Wellness, are vital to thriving social connections. When conflict does develop in a relationship, we have to return to our skill base, listen, listen, and listen some more. We must listen, even when we disagree with, or do not like, what we are hearing. Listening demonstrates respect. Many of us like to say we respect others, but do we *demonstrate* respect? How we move from the state of respect to *demonstrating* respect is to *listen*. We listen with our undivided, undistracted non-verbal attention. We demonstrate respect by using "I" statements to take ownership of our thoughts, beliefs, and feelings, and not projecting with "You" statements, which are accusatory.

We also demonstrate respect when we seek clarification using empathetic statements, and allowing the other person to "set us straight" on their intention, rather than relying on our interpretation of their intention and being inflexible to another possibility. When we consistently use congruent verbal and non-verbal messages, we take giant steps toward regaining trust. Finally, we resolve conflict and show respect when we forgive. How can we ever get back to a strong and supportive relationship with a person after conflict, if we cannot forgive, fully forgive and move on, unfettered. *Get rid of all bitterness, rage and anger, brawling and slander, along with every form of malice. Be kind and compassionate to one another, forgiving each other, just as in Christ God forgave you.*[5]

YOUR WELL WITH GOD JOURNEY

As you reflect on this chapter on Social Wellness, what resonates with you? What can you affirm for yourself and what can you adjust? Is there a specific relationship you want to improve or maintain? How will you do this? Take a moment to write these or other things down to use for your vision board or goal list.

ENDNOTES

1. John 15:13, NIV.
2. 1 Peter 4:10, NIV.
3. Colossians 3:12-13, NIV.
4. Matthew 1:1-2, NIV.
5. Ephesians 4:31-32, NIV.

Chapter 9

SPIRITUAL WELLNESS

"The LORD will guide you always; He will satisfy your needs in a sun-scorched land and will strengthen your frame. You will be like a well-watered garden, like a spring whose waters never fail."

–ISAIAH 58:11, NIV

I n the 1980s there was a popular book titled *All I Really Need to Know, I Learned in Kindergarten* by Robert Fulghum. I love that book! It provides such great common-sense messages to live by. I read that book well before I read the Bible. I read many self-help and inspirational books in my earlier adulthood that truly helped me grow and develop, and dare I say, cope with life. Later, as an adult, when I read the Bible for the first time, I discovered our most profound first lessons for how to live our best life, and I wished I had come to the Bible earlier. One of my favorite scriptures now hangs on my office wall: *But the fruit of the Spirit is love, joy, peace, forbearance, kindness, goodness, faithfulness, gentleness and self-control. Against such things there is no law.*[1]

THE FRUIT OF THE SPIRIT

The fruit of the Spirit is a great starting place to discuss Spiritual Wellness, to discuss God. Spiritual Wellness is recognized in that feeling that we are part of something greater than our physical selves. The inner knowing that we have purpose and essence and following those instincts, which are ultimately God speaking to us through the Holy Spirit. And the Holy Spirit that is planted in us by God bears fruit—nine words to live by. Yet they are not given to us as mere words to live by. They are delicious truths, and we are able to access them within our own free-will at any time to experience spiritual well-being, to experience God. In accessing love, joy, peace, forbearance, kindness, goodness, faithfulness, gentleness and self-control, we are accessing the essence of God, and transforming ourselves into living representations of Him. This is why God, Spiritual Wellness, is at the center of the WELL WITH GOD model. Without God infused in our being, there is no *well*-being—physical is just a body, financial is just money, mental is just thoughts, environmental is just space, occupational is just work, intellectual is just a hobby, and social is just people hanging out together. God, the Spirit, makes these dimensions come to life, have meaning, causes us to yearn for them and gives us drive. We are driven to achieve these dimensions of well-being because they are planted in our DNA by God; but if we take the journey without taking God as our tour guide, we are unfulfilled in them and still seek fulfillment and satisfaction from them. We have it backward at that point. We are to bring the fulfillment and satisfaction to each dimension of wellness by showing up infused and radiating God, the Spirit, in our execution of achieving physical, financial, mental, environmental, occupational, intellectual, and social well-being. In fact, this is where it moves from a thing—*wellness*—to an *essence*—well-being.

Holy Spirit is the wellspring from which our success in the other dimensions of wellness is drawn. We know fulfillment awaits us in all aspects of our lives, or we would not pursue anything and we would not try to make course corrections. We would not know the difference between a good job and a bad one, a tired body from a rested one, financial freedom from indebtedness and greed, etc. Unfortunately, our free will and sin nature cause us to go down wrong roads, get off-track, and spend unnecessary time trying to make corrections. If we do not make our course corrections from a God-centered place, we are on another wrong road, and will continue to be on wrong roads until we get on the right road with God. This can take a little time or this can take a lifetime. This may answer why we repeat the same mistake over and over again. I believe it is when we return to the "mistake" with a

God perspective that we can move forward toward His destination for us. If we purposefully let God work through us, we experience Him and the power we share with Him in getting on the right path. Still, there are times we let the enemy cloud over our free will and dampen all our decisions with pride, jealousy, fear, selfishness, etc.; and God shows up, uninvited, to grace us with His supernatural intervention to get us on the right path. He protects us. Regardless of how He works in our life, the "right path" is only available through God's intervention and presence, invited or uninvited.

CONNECTING WITH GOD

We should not confuse this by thinking God is playing a game with us. He is not. But we may be on a treasure hunt, and He did leave us a large map. It is called the Bible. Everything we need to know for our life is documented in the blueprint of the Bible, not only in the nine fruits of the Spirit, but if that is all we ever read, it is certainly, simply and completely all that we need to know to guide our behavior and achieve well-being.

It occurs to me that God is constantly demonstrating to us that we cannot think of Him in the way our brain has organized mortal thoughts. For example, we do not tend to speak in parables, but God did so all the time. We read a book from beginning to end, but it makes perfect sense to read the Bible from New Testament to Old Testament, or anywhere in between. We do not have to "figure" God out but we do have to take Him out of the neat and tidy box we are often tempted to put Him in, stop thinking of Him linearly, and stop confining His beingness to our limited understanding.

You may be asking, "Why is it so difficult to understand God?," "Why are we made with a sin nature instead of perfect like Him?," "Why is God so hard to understand?" I do not have the answers, but I do believe when I have those questions, they are coming from my linear mind and I am in the box. Or more accurately, I have put Him in the box. At times, those questions have led me to become angry with God. It does not happen frequently, but it does happen. When I become angry with God, I fortunately do not give up on Him, although some of us do give up on God. For me, however, I do not give up; Instead, I start "rethinking" Him. I start thinking I have Him "all wrong," and I start trying to figure Him out. In my younger years, this led me to think God existed in an external place called my "higher power." At another time, I thought God existed in my meditative state, and once I considered whether He existed in a chant. In one recurring practice, I fight the urge to believe God is found in my good deeds or behavior, as though all I have to do is certain actions, and God will do what I want Him to do. I just need to find the checklist, so I can get my boxes checked-off and He can deliver.

All those instances occured when I was stressed and fearful of something. All of those times, God reminded me He cannot be accessed in any of those places; rather, He is accessible *inside* me as the Holy Spirit. Sometimes, I need help returning inward to the Holy Spirit, and I seek the assistance of a pastor or read scripture. These things nudge me back to my center, where I can stop searching externally for God and surrender internally to Him. *Don't you know that you yourselves are God's temple and that God's Spirit dwells in your midst?*[2]

> SOMETIMES, I NEED HELP RETURNING INWARD TO THE HOLY SPIRIT, AND I SEEK THE ASSISTANCE OF A PASTOR OR READ SCRIPTURE

To draw close to God, we have to exercise our spiritual muscles. Otherwise, we leave ourselves vulnerable to the missteps of our free will and the enemy, of our anger, ego, pride, fear, etc. There are many ways and many combinations of ways to work-out with God, to build our spiritual resilience: Silent prayer, praying with others, listening or watching online discussions, reading the Bible, attending church, participating in retreats or conferences, journaling, listening to praise music, tithing, and volunteering. Any or all of the above. Take a moment and think about this list and consider your current "workout" routine with God. Are there one or more of those things are you not doing that you might like to do? Write them down to add to your vision board or goals list.

The most unexpected connection to God for me is reading the Bible. All the other ways of connecting with God were easy for me, but reading the Bible was a daunting "task." Once I did it, however, I was astounded at my closeness and clarity of God and, again, I wished I had read it as a younger woman. As I said before, my approach was all wrong. When I adjusted my course and started with the New Testament, instead of starting at the beginning with the Old Testament, the Bible became easy and enjoyable. I have also learned things that come from the Bible, that I did not realize—sayings, phrases and concepts that I thought were all just clever phrases and good marketing. Surprise! They came from the Bible! For example:

1. "I have escaped only *by the skin of my teeth.*" [3]

2. "Can an Ethiopian *change his skin* or a *leopard its spots?*" [4]

3. "Watch out for false prophets. They come to you in *sheep's clothing*, but inwardly they are ferocious *wolves.*" [5]

The reason I am so fond of the nine fruits of the spirit is that they serve as a guidepost when I waiver in my walk with God. They are the "home base" to which I return when I need to reconnect with the essence of God. However, when I am feeling especially vulnerable to attacks of the enemy it is a different scripture in Ephesians that I use to fight against challenges and help protect my spiritual well-being—the Armor of God.

I referenced it before, but it bears repeating. It is one of my very favorite scriptures. *Therefore put on the full armor of God, so that when the day of evil comes, you may be able to stand your ground, and after you have done everything, to stand. Stand firm then, with the belt of truth buckled around your waist, with the breastplate of righteousness in place, and with your feet fitted with the readiness that comes from the gospel of peace. In addition to all this, take up the shield of faith, with which you can extinguish all the flaming arrows of the evil one. Take the helmet of salvation and the sword of the Spirit, which is the word of God.*[6]

"SUIT UP"

Science-fiction super heroes pale in comparison to the image that the full armor of God brings to my mind. I literally visualize it when I am meditating on this scripture, and it has carried me through some very difficult times. Take a minute and think about what rattles your Spiritual Wellness, be it a person or a scenario. Consider how visualizing yourself "suiting-up" to face each day can help you. God has never failed to provide for me in some way when I have asked for strength or relief. He does not always remove the obstacle, but He always gives me enough relief to make it bearable, or get me through to another day—sometimes to another hour or another minute.

SEEK COUNSEL

Still, armor or no armor, I have at times felt angry or disillusioned with God. When none of my other spiritual workout tools worked, I have sought pastoral counseling—another great spiritual tool. This was typically to help me stay trusting of God during a time when God's timing did not match my expectations. I once met with a pastoral counselor at our church who was a wise woman of 81 years. I know because she told me. She was unbelievably helpful, and at one point when I was in the middle of pouring out my troubles, God spoke to her. I know this, because I recognized a look of consternation that suddenly appeared on her face that matched how I felt whenever I had a sudden word from God. She interrupted my pouring out of troubles, blurting out, "Who haven't you forgiven?" It was out of the blue and a little disarming. "I don't know, eh, nobody," I said. I went on to explain that I don't carry any resentment toward anyone. She seemed unconvinced. I took a stab at it suggesting I had had a disagreement with a coworker, but that was resolved, for the most part. I mentioned my dad and I had a falling out a few years ago, but we had mended that fence and moved on with no problem. I even suggested I am very hard on myself and I don't forgive myself for the mistakes I make sometimes. She still seemed unconvinced but was very gracious. She told me, "Things will turn around for you when you get rid of the unforgiveness." Then, she prayed with me and I never saw her again. Her prophesy would resurface about a year later when I returned to the counseling center with the same issue.

This was during the time I was living four hours away from my husband, separated after Dan was transferred with his company. I had been making the commute every weekend and searching for jobs, to no avail. I didn't mind the commute nearly as much as I minded the constant rejection for jobs that I was well qualified and felt well-suited for. A few of the rejections were surreal and something I could only attribute to God's supernatural "closing of doors." I would be told an offer was coming or I had progressed to the final stage, only to have something out of the blue happen that caused the job to be unavailable, or another person selected without the "next step" that I was told was coming the next week. Toward the end of year two of the job search, I had a prospective employer tell me on the phone, they were putting together an offer for me. A few days later, I received a stale, formatted email that said they selected another person for the position. I was about to leave my office for the day and was reading the message expecting it to be "the offer." I was so defeated that my knees literally buckled when I stood to leave. My chair caught me. No noise came from my mouth, but my eyes began pouring tears like buckets. I did not know how I was going to leave my office without anyone seeing my state, but I managed to do so and get into my car, where I tried to compose myself. I felt punished by God. I felt angry at God. I felt confused by God. I could barely drive, but I left my work parking garage and went to the church. I approached the counseling office and rang the buzzer, hoping everyone had not left for the day, and hoping they would see me without an appointment. A miracle happened. The lead pastor of ministries was returning to his office and walked up to the counseling doors, and when I saw him, he recognized me from a meeting I had with him a year earlier, when we talked about me volunteering to lead some wellness related activities for the church staff. He asked if I had an appointment and I said, "No, but I am hoping to meet with someone." He said, "Everyone has left for the day, but I am happy to meet with you." I am sure I looked a mess, and he was so merciful to respond to my immediacy. I spent about an hour with this pastor, and he was very affirming and helpful. Toward the end of our time together, he said, "Julie, you are looking in a certain direction, but maybe God wants to take you in a different direction. You need to be open to where God is leading you."

I left the meeting, went home, and went to bed, where I lay catatonic in my bed thinking, praying, surrendering, tears flooding my face, staring at the wall through watery puddles. I could not sleep. I lay there for hours. At approximately 2:00 a.m. God finally spoke to me. Not out loud, but He profoundly impressed these words: "When you start respecting your father, everything will open-up for you." More crying, now accompanied by shame. I knew what God was talking about, and at that moment, I also knew what the 81 year old counselor was talking about a year earlier. It was forgiveness. The conflict I thought I had resolved with my dad was not really resolved, and I knew it at this moment. Just because I had stopped giving my 82 year old dad the cold shoulder five years earlier after an 18 month disagreement, and just because I maintained my weekly phone calls with him, did not mean I had gotten over our disagreement. I had not. In fact, I had decided not to respect my dad, choosing to move forward without forgiveness. I did this by calling him weekly with an obligatory heart, and not sharing any relevant details of my life. I protected the information I shared with him, keeping it shallow and random. I knew it and he knew it. And now I was busted, because God knew it too. I felt so ashamed.

FORGIVE

I laid in bed ashamed at my behavior toward my father, and as soon as the day dawned and I thought he would be out of bed and starting his day, I called my father. I could not tell him I had lost respect for him and had never forgiven him, because I know my dad has a tender heart. I knew it would hurt him tremendously to hear those words. Instead, I told him I loved him very much, and knew that all he ever did was with the best intentions, to help the people he loved and even those he did not love. I poured love and affirmation into my dad that day, and told him I had been withholding my own heart from him, and that I was sorry and would not do that anymore.

My dad expressed his deep appreciation for my confession and said he knew I was holding back

UNFORGIVENESS IS POWERFUL ENOUGH TO KEEP US FROM OUR BLESINGS, AND FORGIVENESS IS POWERFUL ENOUGH TO OPEN OURSELVES FURTHER TO GOD'S FAVOR

and he was so happy I was able to work through it. My dad needed to be restored to the pedestal of fatherhood, and I had not realized I had demoted him. God helped me with this, and once the fence was mended with my Earthly father, within two weeks, my Heavenly father opened the door to three jobs, one of which selected me, and I selected them. It was mutual. Unforgiveness is powerful enough to keep us from our blessings, and forgiveness is powerful enough to open ourselves further to God's favor. *Bear with each other and forgive one another if any of you has a grievance against someone. Forgive as the Lord forgave you.*[7]

HEAVEN ON EARTH

I think I experienced Heaven once. It was a millisecond. I think it was Heaven. That is all I can call it, and I am serious when I say it was a millisecond. It was not at any particularly pivotal moment in my life. I was not on the brink of death, and I was not going toward the light with loved ones waiting ahead for me. But, it may have been an out-of-body experience like those who have died and "come-back" to describe it. It occurred a couple of years ago, and when the moment was over, I immediately wanted more. I think about it often with great anticipation and satisfaction.

I was not dreaming but I was in that dreamy, waking state one morning. As I talked about in Chapter Two, God often meets me in the early morning hours, waking me with ideas, answers and comfort. This was one of those times, only this time I experienced what I can only describe as Heaven. At minimum, it was heavenly. For the briefest of moments, I *felt* everything all at the same time—God, Spirit, Jesus, music, voices, color, people, loved ones, space, atmosphere, thoughts, emotions, sensations. I *felt* it all. I saw it all and heard it all, yet only through my feelings, not through my eyes or ears, and there was no conflict between competing sensations that blurred the colors from the music from the people. It was pure fulfillment and joy. I had no physicality, only essence. It was a beautiful kaleidoscope, and in all of that, there was no chaos or distraction. There are literally no other human words to explain what I felt, only *Heaven or heavenly.* As soon as I experienced it, I was full, then it was gone and I wanted more. I even asked God for more, but was immediately sure that I cannot be *there* while I am *here.* But I am certain I will be there again, someday. So will you.

But we can experience a Heaven on Earth, if we nurture, support and exercise our Spiritual Wellness. In so doing, we unlock the anointing God has placed on each of us for each dimension or aspect of our life. Drawing closer to God, we peel away the layers of our sin-nature and experience freedom from the influences of the enemy. Here is where we become WELL WITH GOD. *The heavens declare the glory of God; the skies proclaim the work of his hands. Day after day they pour forth speech; night after night they reveal knowledge.*[8]

YOUR WELL WITH GOD JOURNEY

We are nearing the end of our WELL WITH GOD journey together and you are gathering the concepts for your vision board or goals list. How will you carry God into your pursuit? Take a moment and ask yourself if anything else from this chapter about Spiritual Wellness has resonated with you. What are you still thinking about? Write them down to think about later, meditate or pray on, and consider adding to your vision board.

ENDNOTES

1. Galatians 5:22-23, NIV.

2. 1 Corinthians 3:16, NIV.

3. Job 19:20, NIV.

4. Jeremiah 13:25, NIV.

5. Matthew 7:15, NIV.

6. Ephesians 6:13-17, NIV.

7. Colossians 3:13, NIV.

8. Psalm 19:1-2, NIV.

Conclusion

WELL
WITH
GOD

---

*"God is the seed from which
our well-being springs."*

–JULIE VAN ORDEN

The WELL WITH GOD model is a demonstration and affirmation that God is the seed from which our well-being springs. He is our Source and the path to fulfillment in all dimensions of our wellness. We just have to ask and receive from our heart, knowing that heart-centered asking means we do not control the how and when; but we trust that God hears our prayers and answers them in His perfect will and timing. Through shifting the way we view our path to wellness, we realize fulfillment is unique to each of us in both what wellness looks like and how we get there.

This last chapter will offer two things. It will:

1. Thread God through my personal "Jumanji" experience during the writing of this book in order to illustrate the here and now experience God has for each of us.

2. Tie-up the individual wellness plan we have each been preparing throughout the book, so we may start our own WELL WITH GOD journey.

They have told the church about your love.
Please send them on their way in a manner that honors God.

3 JOHN 1:6, NIV

149

JUMANJI

Wellness is a continual journey, not a destination. After a lifetime of living a wellness lifestyle, it still requires adjustment and growth. A profound demonstration of the WELL WITH GOD model is how it is literally woven into the writing of this book. Writing this book was like the movie *Jumanji* for me. It was scary … at first. Not because I was "writing a book" but because stuff started happening as I was writing the book. Uncomfortable stuff. The chapters literally came to life, in very challenging ways, as I was penning them. I noticed the trend fairly early. I realized I had to return to the first dimension, Physical Wellness, to make edits after I had an adverse biometric screening result during my annual physical exam with my doctor. My biometrics did not match my health practices, and I had to revisit my personal nutrition regimen and make some unexpected adjustments. Unexpected, because I had a plan, and I was nudged by God to consider a different plan. Trusting God's impression, I did my research, spoke with a few people, and applied a completely different strategy. This caused me to achieve some outcomes that I did not realize I needed, and has helped me reset what is possible for myself physically.

I returned to edit the second dimension, Financial Wellness, when my husband, Dan, was laid off from work, illuminating new insights I needed to share with readers. This "scare" led to immediate prayer and an unbelievable level of peace for both Dan and me, despite more than half of our family income being deleted from our household budget in one afternoon. Thus, I moved it from something I was afraid of to something I was at peace with. This incident, however, increased my suspicion that God may not just be helping me find the *words* to write this book using historical experiences; He may be challenging me to *live* new experiences, so I could write from a more recent place of vulnerability and a deeper testimony. With this epiphany, I closed my eyes and leaped. "God, I am willing to go where you need me to go in order to get this right and truly help others be WELL WITH GOD." Then I mused to myself, "Be careful what you pray for, Julie, God has been known to take you on some intense learning experiences." And so, He continued to do so.

I got up close and personal with the third dimension, Mental Wellness, three months after Dan was laid off. Dan had just received a job offer for a short-term contract of 6-8 months with a major airline. Praise! It was a dream job for him, kind-of a bucket list opportunity—to work for a major airline. I had not realized I felt weighted by the layoff, because I was truly at peace with it. But when the contract happened, I felt a gentle weight lift. I immediately wanted to eat carbs (don't ask), I felt like socializing again, I was giddy, I had more swagger, I wanted to shop, I wanted a margarita and I literally was holding my head higher. Less than 48 hours into this "lightness," I had a restless night's sleep, and awoke at about 2:00 a.m. knowing something was wrong. The feeling I had when Dan was laid off was so comforting, I immediately wanted to return to that grounding with God, and I was aware I had stepped out from under God's steadying hand. I had let the impending financial windfall from Dan's new job give way to the enemy, luring me with feelings of impulsiveness.

I knew (I know) God doesn't mind when we buy nice things for ourselves, but I also knew I had stepped over the line of stewardship to impulsiveness. Yet it was not too late. I had not gone on any eating or spending sprees, but I *was* on a spiritual spree and flirting with getting truly off-track. I was not grounded and I was aware of it. I prayed for God to keep His steadying hand on me, and in the back of my mind I mused again, "Be careful what you ask for. He is a good God and delivers, just not in the way you want, usually in a new challenge or learning experience." That challenge literally occurred six hours later when I was in an 8:30 a.m. meeting, and my boss announced that our company was going to be laying off a large part of our workforce, starting the next week with voluntary layoffs. I felt okay for about 20 minutes, processing it as a teammate with a job to do, reminding myself that God's got this ... then I started to panic. Dan had just gotten a contract job but it was only for six months. It had taken two years for God to bring me *this* job, that I may well be losing after only one year of employment. If I was not working in six months and Dan's contract was over in six months, we would be in deep water! I felt immediately nauseous.

I returned to my office, tied up a few tasks, and decided I was going to have to go home and be catatonic for the rest of the day. Seriously and literally. I felt panicked, and I decided to stay panicked ... at home. My Mental Wellness was sinking fast and I needed personal space. I got my things ready to leave for the day but decided to stop in on a colleague, Rosanne, across the hall who was on my team and had also been in the same meeting with me. I stood in front of Rosanne's desk where she was seated and I told her, "This is kind of freaking me out." She said "Yeah, it's scary." I got a little moisture in my eyes and said, "I think I have to go home." Rosanne stunned me. She said firmly, yet kindly, "No." Mind you, Rosanne is not my boss and was not over-ruling my decision as an authority figure. She is a colleague, part of my Social Wellness system at my worksite, and she is sitting at her desk looking up at me and calmly saying, "No." Nothing else. I was dumbfounded. I retorted pathetically, "I feel nauseous and I literally think I need to throw up."

In the same calm, firm tone, Rosanne said, "You can go to your office and throw up." Still stunned, I persisted, "I need some time to pray and just process this." Rosanne said, "Pray in your office. This is for you. I am telling you to stay here and be effective. Right now, we have jobs, let's keep them." At that moment, I stepped back under God's steadying hand on my shoulder. I knew Rosanne was right, I gave her a huge thank you, a double high five across her desk, returned to my office and got back to work. More importantly, I had this jolt to stop thinking of how this could affect *me*, and remember who I am—the company's wellness coordinator; and people needed to be inspired to be resilient, and that was part of my job. I wanted to be embarrassed for a moment about the momentary break in my Mental and Spiritual Wellness, but I resisted the selfish urge and moved-on to be a part of the healing process at work. I would wait in faithful anticipation of finding out what God had in store for my Occupational Wellness in 4-5 weeks when the involuntary layoffs would begin. I also returned to Rosanne's office at the end of the day and said, "I do not know what your spiritual beliefs are Rosanne, but I believe God is very strong in you." She replied with a knowing smile and that same steady voice, "I think so."

My Environmental Wellness was challenged for months throughout the writing of this book as I struggled with my inability to communicate well with some of my work colleagues. The job was great, the company was great but I did not have a natural connection and felt out of place. I was faltering rather than thriving. It took a long year, but I settled into a workable environment with my colleagues, just in time to experience the company's force reduction together and come out on the other side with our team intact, much lighter in spirit and more genuinely connected.

Through the threat and reality of layoffs for both my husband and myself during my writing of this book, I gained profound insight into the fourth dimension, Occupational Wellness. I shifted how I saw myself fit in. Previously, I had concluded that my calling in the health and wellness field was more richly satisfied when I was working in industries that were "people-centric," such as academia, health and social services, etc. This was the only type work setting I had known. Then God supernaturally closed every open door to jobs in the industries I thought were more suitable for me, and He led me to this job, where I was hired to develop a new wellness program for a publicly traded company. It was the same type of work, only in a different industry. Even though my team was located in the Human Resources department, there was a different culture when working in Human Resources at a people-centric organization than working in Human Resources for a Fortune 500 company. I felt like a Martian. I spoke from a different skill-set, and I operated from a different passion. Yet, through this discovery, God reminded me that my work is not in the industry's business model, it is in my knowledge and gifts to serve people, and serving people exists every day, with every individual who crosses my path at work. This revelation has helped me be a better person, more consistently, whether I am at work or out in the community.

My Intellectual Wellness was challenged during this process in an interesting "opposite" way—not through something that happened to me, but through the absence of something. My intellectual interests lie in self-development activities and inspiring true stories of triumph. During the writing of this book, I chose not to read other people's books, lest I be influenced by their experience instead of drawing on my own authentic experiences. Other than our regular church attendance, scripture readings and historical church messages, I avoided gaining inspiration from anywhere other than God, and He delivered in a big way! This helped me remain open and receptive to God alone, and the journey He had for me through this book. I started to see myself as the source of inspiration for others, instead of seeking to be inspired. This is how my Jumanji experience, my creativity, was fully realized.

I shared previously that Social Wellness has always come naturally for me. As we know, God can take anything higher and what He has done for me through the experiences I have had writing this book is most profoundly realized in my 34 year marriage to Dan. By all accounts, we have had a close, blessed marriage. He is the foundation of my social support network. It has been so good, that I did not know marriage could get better. Then God showed up ... again. Remember when I mused, "Be careful what you pray for?" Every day I leave for work ahead of Dan. Before leaving the house, I sit on the edge of the bed, take his hand and pray with him for our day. I always ask God to bring us closer to Him. The day Dan told me he was laid off, I immediately thought, *Be careful what you pray for. I prayed to be closer to God and we are about to get ever closer.*

God did not disappoint. After being laid-off, Dan began his own journey reading the Bible for the first time ever, and it came to life for Him, but not in the *Jumanji* way. The best part is, he brought his journey into our marriage by opening up conversation, relating it to scripture, and for the first time in our marriage, Dan began to pray out loud with me, including taking my hand in his. I thought we had a blessed marriage. This took us to an entirely different level! It took me by surprise. Dan was always a good man, believed in God, attended church, served and helped others, had a compassionate heart, etc., but I was the spiritual leader in our home; and to be honest with you, at times, I felt like an alien. No longer. We are both "all-in" with God, and the energy in our lives has elevated. Our support for one another spills out to others differently, too. Dan went from zero to 100% in sharing God's grace in his life, tying experiences to God's plan, relating scripture to current events and sharing perspectives that enlighten and inspire me in my own journey.

WE ARE BOTH "ALL-IN" WITH GOD, AND THE ENERGY IN OUR LIVES HAS ELEVATED

CLOSING THE GAP

My spiritual challenge, and subsequent growth, throughout writing this book has been in "closing the gap." I think this can be a useful description, and even provides a visual image for others, not just for myself. What does "closing the gap" mean? It means I am closing the gap between life events and *when* I turn to God for guidance and consultancy. My relationship with God has been great most of my life, although His place at times has been a moving target. Early in my life, it was easy for me to initially go to God when I was struggling and at my wits end and I *needed* Him. Otherwise, "Don't call me, I'll call you." Then I progressed to being able to recognize His divine intervention, and give Him thanks. As I continued to grow in faith, I walked daily with Him, but there still remained a gap between us. But, the gap was closing. I told you I was meditating and God laid it on my heart to write this book. So, I started later that same day, but He had to remind me a few times before I got busy. I also told you when my boss told our team about impending layoffs, I kind of lost my focus for about 30 minutes. I know that is not a long time-frame, but the fact remained, I was closing the gap.

> I AM CLOSING THE
> GAP BETWEEN LIFE
> EVENTS AND *WHEN*
> I TURN TO GOD
> FOR GUIDANCE

I truly closed the gap between God and myself during an incident resulting in injury. I was using my sewing machine to alter a skirt, and my finger got in the way, and the needle when straight into my finger nail and so deep into my finger that I was fairly certain it cleared the other side, thread and all. Not kidding. Something supernatural happened at that moment and it was not shock. I was, for a lack of a better term, unfazed. My clarity was crisp. I unplugged the machine with my free hand because the other hand was tethered to the machine with a needle sticking through it. I didn't want to accidentally step on the pedal and cause the needle to move. I calmly and loudly called for my husband who was two rooms away. While I waited, I moved the skirt out of the way so I didn't get blood on it. I tried to back-out the needle, but it would not budge. I called my husband a second time. I started to loosen the needle head from the locked position in the machine so I could move my hand away from the machine and maybe Dan would be able to pull it out with pliers. I called for Dan again, who was on a ladder painting the ceiling, and now I could hear his feet descending the metal. *Good, he was on his way.* I could not get the needle head from the locked position.

Dan arrived and momentarily assessed the situation, and asked if I could back it out, and I decided to try that again. The needle slipped out. At the bathroom sink, we doctored my finger with alcohol, hydrogen peroxide, bacterial ointment and a bandage. Dan ensured that there was no thread left in my finger and he examined the blood level on the needle determining that although it did not pierce through to the other side, it was close. Fifteen minutes from start to finish, I was back at my sewing machine finishing my project.

That evening Dan remarked several times how I didn't cry, I didn't panic, I didn't curse, I didn't wrench in pain, and I didn't get anxious. After 34 years of marriage, Dan knows my *modus operandi*. Anxious and panicked would have been typical and, in this case, maybe warranted. I told him all I could think of from the moment it happened was, "God is here and together we can work with this unfortunate situation. It's going to be fine." And it was. This is when I realized that I had closed the gap between calling upon God and being present with Him in the sowing and in the piercing. It was a pivotal moment for me. *But whoever is united with the Lord is one with him in spirit.*[1]

NEXT STEPS IN YOUR WELL WITH GOD JOURNEY

Throughout reading this book, you have been hearing stories, learning skills, making connections, relating to situations, marveling at God's role in our creation, and writing down concepts that resonate with you. Your notes, by the way, are God's impressions on your heart. They are straight from Him. Now, it is time to bring His vision, and yours, to life. Let us get started:

1. **Make a vision board within 24 hours.** If you are going to change your behavior and bring about your vision, you have to put a plan into action while you have momentum. Using your

own supplies, a large piece of cardboard, a poster board from the office supply store or any other creative medium available to make your vision board. You want positive, appealing images or words that represent each goal you have set, so scour magazine clippings, create your own images or print-out from the internet. Make sure you have at least one representation for every dimension of wellness. Create a collage of your vision by gluing the images on your board but make sure you put your representation of God at the center of your masterpiece.

2. **For each dimension, write down *how* you plan to attain each vision.** List three steps to get started toward your vision and add them to your vision board.

3. **For each dimension add a representation of *why* each goal is important to you.** For example, I have images of a runner and a golfer on my vision board because I want to stay fit. The reason I want to stay fit is depicted in another image of a book and a person speaking before an audience. I want to be credible in the wellness profession, and in order to do so, I have to engage in my own brand of fitness.

4. **Place it somewhere you can view it regularly.** Frame your vision board, if you like. Say a prayer over your vision board and put your vision into God's hands. Prepare to receive.

5. **Show your vision board to someone and tell them what each of the images or words represent.** Doing this creates built-in accountability. My mother-in-law was visiting from out-of-town once when I made a vision board. I framed it and placed in on a wall near the entrance of my bedroom. The next day, she asked what I had made the evening before and wanted to know about

it. She had never heard of or seen a vision board. It was a great way to share my aspirations with her and maybe even dispel any suspicions that I am actually the devil who stole her son! Just kidding. My mother-in-law did an amazing job raising that man to be a most loving and generous husband. I see her sweet influence all over his wonderful nature.

6. **Talk about your visions and what you plan to achieve.** Speak it into existence, as the saying goes. And, don't forget to talk about your God and how He delivers favor to all those who trust, believe and follow Him.

When God started to lay the WELL WITH GOD model on my heart, He clearly let me know He is at the core of all the dimensions of wellness. Hopefully you have noticed, the dimensions encompass all aspects of our lives. Nothing is missing. All of life falls into the eight-point model, and God is at the core of all of life. I know this is not a new revelation. Religious scholars have illustrated since Biblical times that God is the center of it all. Yet, how often do we give it all to God? How many times have we heard the concept mind, body, and spirit, and tied them together and gone to God to achieve our total wellness? This is the *time*. *This is the time to be* WELL WITH GOD. *But seek first his kingdom and his righteousness, and all these things will be given to you as well.*[2]

ENDNOTES

1. 1 Corinthians 6:17, NIV.
2. Matthew 6:33, NIV.

GOD IS THE SEED
FROM WHICH
OUR WELL-BEING
SPRINGS.

JULIE VAN ORDEN, MHA

Julie Anna Van Orden holds a Master of Health Administration degree from Chapman University, a private, nonprofit university in Orange, California and a Bachelor of Science degree in Health Science from Arizona State University in Tempe, Arizona. She has three industry credentials/certificates issued by the National Wellness Institute (NWI): Certified Wellness Practitioner, Certificate-Worksite Wellness Program Manager, and Certificate-Worksite Wellness Specialist. Julie also has Faculty designation with the Wellness Council of America (WELCOA) and has over 30 years of experience in the health and wellness industry.

Julie is a trained communication skills facilitator and domestic mediator. She has taught hundreds of communication skills training sessions and has mediated hundreds of child custody agreements in the State of Maryland. She has been a keynote speaker, session leader and guest panelist for multitudes of state, local and companywide education sessions. While living in the Florida Keys with her career-military husband, Dan, Julie co-hosted a local weekly cable television show for parenting called, *Quality Time*.

After seeing *West Side Story* when Julie was 10 years old, she prayed for God to bring her a Puerto Rican husband—Dan turns out to be half Puerto Rican, so God truly delivers! The couple have been happily married since 1986. Google her story on YouTube, "I Prayed for a Puerto Rican."

Julie and Dan are members of Gateway Church (Southlake campus) in the Dallas-Ft. Worth metroplex, where they volunteer in the Marriage Challenge Ministry. They have one daughter, Tess, who is their favorite topic of conversation because she is so fabulous and clever. Tess lives with her equally fabulous and dashingly handsome husband, Adam, in San Antonio, TX. Julie and Dan currently have two kitties—Ricky and @HavanaCubaGoodingJunior who has his own Instagram page.

Julie is available to speak at your event and is qualified to share on many topics. She also hosts seminars which you can attend live, or partner with her to bring to your area. For more information visit:

WELLWITHGOD.COM

SEMINARS

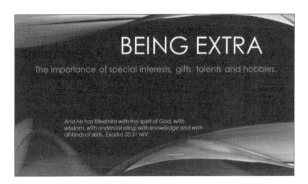

BEING EXTRA–INTELLECTUAL WELLNESS

In addition to our destined profession in life, God has prepared us with creative, analytical and intellectual gifts to enjoy that may or may not be associated with our profession. Discover how these gifts are meant to enhance and broaden our life's experience and bring us additional fulfillment as we achieve Intellectual well-being.

COMFORTABLE IN OUR OWN SKIN– PHYSICAL WELLNESS

We are each perfectly and wonderfully made by God. These are not just affirming words, they are Truth. The journey to Physical well-being through fitness, nutrition and rest is often found in the most unexpected path. Find your path!

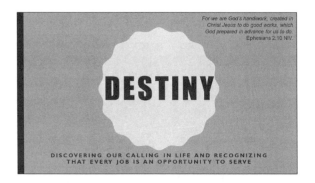

DESTINY–OCCUPATIONAL WELLNESS

Discover what you were meant to do with your life! From stay-at-home moms, to skilled vocations, to the C-Suite in a Fortune 500 company; God has prepared each of us with a divine set of skills to achieve success and find joy in our God-inspired profession.

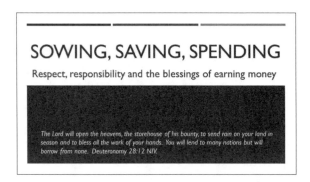

SOWING, SAVING, SPENDING–FINANCIAL WELLNESS

We may not all become millionaires because God does not put a millionaire's heart in each of us. Still, God does intend each of us to live in abundance and financial security. Financial wellness explores attitudes about poverty and wealth and the behaviors associated with those attitudes. Unlock your path to abundance.

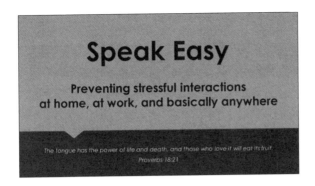

SPEAK EASY–ENVIRONMENTAL WELLNESS

Become an exceptional communicator and find out what God tells us about how we interact with others! Environmental wellness is not about being green, it is about creating personal and professional work environments where people can share, grow and thrive, in good times and in bad. The foundation for this is good communication! In this session, learn the 2 foundations, 4 styles, 6 skills & 4 boosters to becoming an exceptional communicator and fostering the same in others!

STRESS MASTERS–MENTAL WELLNESS

Stress definitely affects our Mental well-being. Understand God's intentions for us when it comes to stress, explore the 4 types of stress, how it affects us, and learn the most productive tool for working through stress!

TRIBE- SOCIAL WELLNESS

God wants us to have a strong Social support system – our tribe! Learn how to achieve Social well-being through meaningful healthy relationships with others whether you are an introvert, an extrovert or anywhere in between! Explore the Stroke Bank Theory and how our self-esteem ebbs and flows according to our interactions with others.

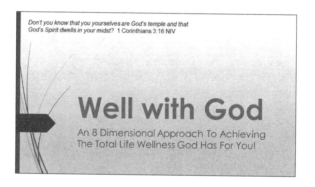

WELL WITH GOD–SPIRITUAL WELLNESS

God has prepared a life of total well-being for each of us. While there are common pathways, no two are identical. Find your unique path through deepening your relationship with God and let Him reveal all you can be!

WELLWITHGOD.COM

NOTES

NOTES

NOTES

WELLWITHGOD.COM

"*He is before all things, and in Him
all things hold together.*"

–COLOSSIANS 1:17, NIV